Agricultural Sciences for the Developing Nations

A symposium presented at
the Cleveland meeting
of the American Association for
the Advancement of Science
29 and 30 December 1963

Edited by ALBERT H. MOSEMAN
Director for Agricultural Sciences
The Rockefeller Foundation, New York

Publication No. 76 of the
American Association
for the Advancement of Science
Washington, D. C. 1964

Preface

Agricultural Sciences for the Developing Nations is based on four half-day sessions organized by the Section on Agriculture of the American Association for the Advancement of Science, held during the 130th annual meeting of the Association in Cleveland, Ohio, on 29 and 30 December, 1963. The symposium was sponsored jointly with the American Society for Microbiology and the AAAS Committee on Desert and Arid Zones Research.

The symposium was devoted to the role of agricultural science and technology in the acceleration of economic progress in newly developing nations, and was organized under the following major topics: (1) characteristics of agricultural systems in emerging nations; (2) research to devise and adapt innovations; (3) education and development of human resources; (4) establishing indigenous institutions to serve advancing agriculture.

Participants were chosen on the basis of their knowledge and experience in research and education in agriculture and their concern with agricultural developments abroad.

Serving with me as co-chairmen of the individual sessions were: Roland Renne, Assistant Secretary of Agriculture, U.S. Department of Agriculture; W. M. Myers, Dean of International Programs, University of Minnesota; R. M. Kottman, Dean, College of Agriculture and Home Economics, The Ohio State University; and J. A. Rigney, Campus Coordinator, North Carolina State College Agricultural Development Project for Peru. Howard B. Sprague of The Pennsylvania State University (now with the Agricultural Board, National Academy of Sciences), Secretary of the AAAS Section on Agriculture, assisted with the organization of the program and arrangements for the meeting.

The importance of agricultural and rural development in the advancement of levels of living in low-income countries is increasingly recognized as new nations gain experience in economic de-

iii

velopment processes. Many of the emerging nations are faced with the task of transforming a subsistence level agricultural system into a more productive contributor to national economic growth at a time when their rate of population increase is placing unprecedented demands on national capacities for the production of food and fiber. Countries with annual population growth rates of 3 per cent or more are confronted with the formidable challenge of improving agricultural output sufficiently beyond future subsistence levels to realize the essential contribution of agricultural productivity to total economic progress.

Although materials and methods from agriculturally advanced nations can seldom be transferred directly to developing nations without testing and adaptation to local environments, the evaluation of factors that have contributed to agricultural progress in the United States is useful in isolating principles or procedures that may help to accelerate agricultural development elsewhere. These factors are numerous, interrelated, and complex, but they have permitted achievement of an abundance and efficiency in the agricultural sector such as developing nations aspire to as they strive for economic, social, and political stability.

A hundred years ago about 70 per cent of the total labor force of the United States was engaged in agriculture, a proportion not unlike that of the rural population of many of the emerging nations. Today the United States has only 7 per cent of its labor force employed on farms. From 1870 to 1930 most of the increase in farm productivity came from the expanded use of land and labor. The growth rate in agricultural production slowed markedly during the 1930's, when unfavorable weather and depressed prices caused many farm people to move to urban areas and into non-agricultural pursuits. This added labor supply for manufacturing, transportation, construction, and various service industries helped immeasurably to advance the mechanization and "industrialization" of agriculture.

The era of most rapid progress in agricultural development in the United States, the past 30 years, has been marked by the steady infusion of science and technology. Increased productivity from improved materials and technics, rather than from more land and farm labor, accounted for about three-fourths of the expansion in agricultural output. Nevertheless, the annual increase in farm output in the United States has rarely exceeded 2 per cent. Since many developing nations face the task of meeting needs of populations that are growing at rates of more than 3 per cent annually, it is evident that the most effective measures that can be assembled must be applied promptly in modernizing their agricultural practices.

Local and national governments must establish the basic economic and social conditions that will encourage farmers to expand production. Among these are systems of land tenure, stable and adequate prices for farm products, accessible and dependable markets, and supplies of consumer goods that enhance levels of living. External agencies may be helpful primarily in furnishing the kinds of support and technical assistance that are involved most directly in expanding production.

It is hoped that this book will be helpful in furnishing some background of experience for the use of agricultural planners in the newly emerging nations.

ALBERT H. MOSEMAN, *Editor*
1963 Chairman,
AAAS Section on Agriculture

Contributors

FREDERICK N. ANDREWS, Vice President for Research and Dean of the Graduate School, Purdue University, Lafayette, Indiana

RICHARD BRADFIELD, Special Consultant, The Rockefeller Foundation, New York, and Professor Emeritus of Soil Science, Cornell University, Ithaca, New York

HAROLD R. CAPENER, Professor, Department of Agricultural Economics and Rural Sociology, The Ohio State University, Columbus, Ohio

R. D. FRAZIER, Graduate Research Assistant, Department of Agronomy, Purdue University, Lafayette, Indiana; formerly Agronomist, Purdue-Brazil Project

F. F. HILL, Vice President, International Programs, The Ford Foundation, New York

CHARLES E. KELLOGG, Deputy Administrator for Soil Survey, Soil Conservation Service, United States Department of Agriculture, Washington, D. C.

ERVEN J. LONG, Director, Rural Development Service, Office of Technical Cooperation and Research, Agency for International Development, United States Department of State, Washington, D. C.

ALBERT H. MOSEMAN, Director for Agricultural Sciences, The Rockefeller Foundation, New York

J. B. PETERSON, Head, Department of Agronomy, Purdue University, Lafayette, Indiana

RALPH W. PHILLIPS, Director, International Organizations Staff, Office of the Assistant Secretary for International Affairs, United States Department of Agriculture, Washington, D. C.

THEODORE W. SCHULTZ, Professor of Economics, The University of Chicago, Chicago, Illinois

ERNEST W. SPRAGUE, Geneticist, The Rockefeller Foundation, New Delhi, India

DAVID B. WILLIAMS, Director, International Student Office, Cornell University, Ithaca, New York

vii

Contents

Characteristics of Agricultural

Systems in Emerging Nations

Institutional Factors Limiting Progress in the Less Developed Countries

ERVEN J. LONG

Director, Rural Development Service, Office of Technical Cooperation and Research, Agency for International Development, United States Department of State, Washington, D. C.

THE TOPIC originally assigned for this paper was "Institutions for Agricultural Science, Technology, and Service in Developing Nations." With the consent of Dr. Moseman, who developed the program for this symposium, and our Chairman, Dr. Renne, I have changed the title to "Institutional Factors Limiting Progress in the Less Developed Countries," and in so shortening the title, enlarged the topic. I did so deliberately because, in the less developed countries, the special characteristics and problems which influence the effectiveness of institutions of agricultural science and technology derive principally from the general social and economic institutions of the country. By and large, in these countries the institutions of agricultural science and technology, and even the so-called "service" institutions, are historical transplants from a more advanced country, either directly borrowed by self-governing countries, or inserted into those countries under colonial rule. Therefore, the extent to which these institutions are less effective than in their parent countries results primarily from the fundamental characteristics of the country of which they are a part.

In the more advanced countries such as our own and those of western Europe, the institutions of agricultural science and technology are, inherently, genuine participants in their respective countries' national development processes, because they themselves grew directly out of those development processes. They were

The views expressed in this paper are those of the writer and not necessarily those of the Agency for International Development.

3

born out of the labor of development, took their shape and role from the needs of development, have been judged and supported in accordance with their contributions to development. In short, they are, and have been from the first, a central dynamic, organically internal part of the agricultural development process.

Not so, unfortunately, in the underdeveloped countries. There, such institutions have been developed to serve different roles, have been a part—largely an almost extraneous part—of a totally different type of society.

For these countries, the present is a period of profound transition. This must be a transition in the relationship of these institutions to their societies, not just changes in the institutions of science and technology themselves. This transition will call for the creation of some new, and radical modification of many existing, social and economic institutions, not normally considered a part of the formal institutions of agricultural science, technology, and service. Without such changes institutions of science will remain external skin grafts, adhering to, but not participating effectively in the development of, the societies of which they are a part. In short, in the absence of fundamental institutional changes throughout these societies, agricultural science will continue to preach its sermons to an empty house.

I believe that we must address ourselves to this basic issue, otherwise we shall be concerned with symptoms, not causes—with peripheral, not central issues.

I wish now to assert two underlying, basic propositions—propositions which I believe can be well supported but which time does not permit me to validate fully today.

The first proposition is that *economic underdevelopment is itself largely a consequence of institutional underdevelopment.* It is a result of institutions' being either nonexistent, inadequate, or improperly oriented to meet the needs of economic progress. In fact, there appears to be virtually no correlation of either the rate or the level of development with the resource endowments of a country. And there is even little, if any, correlation between development rates and the availability of hard currency capital. A glance at the underdevelopment of the petroleum and mineral rich countries of Africa and the Near East will confirm this observation. Indeed, the type and level of institutional and human resource development appear to be about the only reliable indicators of progress.

On the subject of the present discussion, wisdom begins with the recognition that the institutional structures of the truly underdeveloped societies were evolved through the centuries to accommodate social objectives other than progress. Though it is an oversimplification, it is probably not greatly inaccurate to characterize the prime objective of such institutional structures as being *survival*—survival of the group, the society, the tribe, rather than of the individual.

I believe it is an axiom of biology that no species can survive unless it has achieved an accommodation to its ecological environment, and that this accommodation results in a system of restraints upon the species which keep it from getting out of hand. We often cover this concept under the term "nature's balance." Similar accommodations to their environments have been made by human societies. Since humans are intelligent, these accommodations are not purely biological; they have grown out of usage, and take the form of customs, sanctions, and laws of the society and of attitudes, motives, habits, and practices of the people. The entire institutional structure of a typical truly underdeveloped society, thus evolved to ensure survival of the group, does so by discouraging individual initiative which might risk survival of the group, by discouraging change which might threaten established order, by limiting decision making to the few conservative ruling elders rather than spreading it broadly or entrusting it to those young enough to be apt to try out new and dangerous ideas. In short, most institutions in underdeveloped countries are characterized by a specific forfeiture of progress in the interest of survival.

The Renaissance in Europe, culminating in the industrial revolution, shifted the goals of the human enterprise in Western societies —from survival through order, to progress through change. It is important to recognize that, even though centuries were required, the rupture of the institutional fabric of those societies necessitated by this shift in goals was so profound that history records it as an industrial "revolution."

The acceptance of *progress* as the central organizing ideal of human endeavor swept across western Europe and into much of the New World with amazing speed and thoroughness, two and more centuries ago. Strangely enough, however, it left almost untouched until the last few decades the great masses of people living in what we now refer to as the underdeveloped societies. The prevailing attitudes and institutions of these countries are still largely pointed toward realization of ancient objectives.

But the concept of progress as an ideal has now caught hold in even the most remote nations. It is awakening the consciousness of the people in the huts, and even the consciences of the people in the palaces. As a political imperative, this commitment to progress by most underdeveloped societies is irrevocable. It remains to be seen, however, whether the depth of this commitment is fully understood by the emerging nations which have thus changed their primary objectives and, in so doing, their national values—whether, as Dr. José Marull has put it, they fully understand the price they must pay for the progress they seek.[1]

For this leads to our second general proposition, that *countries wishing to jump into the stream of economic progress must be willing fundamentally to alter their institutional structures.* By its very nature, this proposition cannot be stated as a categorical imperative; it is relative, and meaningless apart from a specific reference. Nevertheless, it is clear that social, economic, and political institutions developed through an ageless past to achieve accommodation *to* an environment are ill equipped to serve as vehicles of controlled and creative transformation *of* the environment to serve human ends. It is important that those of us concerned with the development process face this issue squarely and choose sides, as it were, between the view that American and other so-called Western institutions cannot be transplanted, and the view that economic development of the less developed countries requires essentially this very process.

It is popular to say that our institutions must be "adapted, not adopted." This is, of course, true on its face. But what does it mean? Does it mean that we start from the premise that existing institu-

---

[1] José Marull, in "Discussion" of the writer's paper "The world agricultural situation as related to political and social trends," *Proceedings, World Food Forum, Commemorating Centennial U.S. Department of Agriculture, 1862–1962,* p. 104, Washington, D. C.

tional structures in underdeveloped countries are essentially sound and require only a little tinkering? Or does it mean merely that, obviously, we must properly accommodate the institutional transplants to their new settings in order to make them take root and grow into viable structures?

In my opinion, much of our country's success as a stimulator of progress depends upon the proper resolution of this basic decision. For if the earlier analysis is sound, *the institutional transformations and development called for in a typical underdeveloped country will be deep, profound, and far reaching.* To be sure, what will emerge will not look much like the U.S.A.; but if progress is to be the objective, the resulting institutions will differ even more profoundly in their fundamentals from those which now characterize those countries. It is not for us to say whether or not other nations should pay the price which such profound institutional reconstructions will demand. This is their choice. But intellectual honesty requires the recognition that economic progress has its price, and that this price is the deep-going transformation of inherited institutions, developed for other purposes, into a new set which will serve as effective vehicles of change and development.

THREE CATEGORIES OF INSTITUTIONAL IMPEDIMENTS TO RURAL PROGRESS

Space does not permit a cataloguing, much less an analysis, of all the institutions which must be either created or changed in order to achieve the necessary transformation of a typical underdeveloped society. Instead, I shall attempt merely a simple classification, with illustrations, of some of the types of institutional impediments to rural development of typical underdeveloped countries.

Institutions Which Inhibit the Play of Incentives

It flows almost as a conclusion from the foregoing discussion that institutions typical of an underdeveloped country inhibit the play of *incentives* in encouraging individual initiative—incentives to work hard, to save, to invest, to innovate, to take risks, to acquire skills. Pointed as they are toward the survival of the species, these institutions place the emphasis on stability and security for the group rather than on rewards for innovations to the individual. This emphasis is not achieved by any single institution, but by an interlocked system of institutions which work in concert to achieve this one general result.

Land tenure institutions are, classically, considered to be at the heart of this basic problem in many of the underdeveloped countries. Labor is so plentiful, and off-farm job opportunities are so limited, that ownership of land carries with it almost complete control over the lives of the landless. If the tenant chooses to work a little harder, or invest some of his savings in his farm, he must share heavily with his landlord the fruits of his extra labor. This if he is lucky, if he has some economic or political bargaining power. More often than not, and given a little time, the landowner finds ways of absorbing virtually all the extra production for himself. Thus the tenant learns not to smile, lest the landlord raise his rent; as the Eastern proverb has it, "A smile on the face of a tenant speaks of the stupidity of his landlord."

There are, however, other institutions which work with equal effect to deaden the play of incentives. The *credit system* often holds farmers in total bondage to the moneylenders, sometimes for money borrowed by long-dead ancestors of the indebted farmers. Interest rates often run 100 per cent or higher per year. Illiterate villagers frequently have to rely on the moneylender's calculations, which are not always made with scrupulous honesty. Worse still, very little of the credit serves the useful purpose of making the farmer more productive. Most underdeveloped societies accord high esteem to ceremonies; in some countries over half the money borrowed by farm families is spent on weddings, funerals, and the like. And of that which is spent for so-called "production" purposes, rather little really finds its way into improved farming, so that the credit does nothing but keep the farmer in debt. A study with which the writer was associated in India indicated that not more than 5 to 10 per cent of the short-term investment—what economists call "variable capital"—was used in a way that increased the farmer's productivity, and hence his total income. This heavy burden of indebtedness for unproductive credit obviously discourages the farmer from making productive investments, or any kind of innovation which requires even a little capital, by soaking up his potential savings and cutting off possibilities for additional borrowing.

The *pricing and marketing systems*, or lack thereof, also destroy the play of incentives for the farmer to work, to invest, or to innovate. Most underdeveloped countries have only rudimentary pricing and marketing systems. Prices for identical products often vary widely from village to nearby village. They vary even more widely from village to city, and more widely still from time to time. Farmers commonly do not know of higher prices in other nearby areas or more distant cities. If they do know, they often cannot take advantage of higher prices elsewhere, as they are bound by prior understandings, socially more compelling than contracts, to sell to the moneylender in whose debt they are. And their resources are far too meager, even if they had storage facilities, to await the higher prices which will come when today's production gluts give way to tomorrow's famine. Thus the entire marketing and pricing system works against inducing proper investments at and before planting time, as the promise of future gain beckons only weakly and from great distance through the fog of uncertainty which enshrouds the typical farmer's price expectations. The problem is not, in most countries, so much that of prices' being too low or of marketing margins' being too high; it is primarily that of the farmer's uncertainty as to what the prices will be and, especially, as to who will get the higher prices—he, the landlord, or the moneylender.

The type of social organization—the greater family or the tribe—also profoundly affects the play of incentives. We Americans take for granted a concept of family organization which applies powerful leverage upon the primary family head to strive on behalf of himself, and his wife and children. This is not, however, the norm in the underdeveloped countries. Rewards for unusual effort do not normally go to the man who makes it, even though he receives the money in the first instance, but to an elder or chieftain who distributes it through a tangled skein of family or tribal relations. Indeed, extreme social censure is brought to bear on anyone who holds for himself any appreciable portion of the rewards for his own extra effort. True enough, in some societies the individual appears to be motivated to work for the greater family or tribe rather than for himself or his immediate family; but this motivation is probably more apparent than real. In any event, the entire greater family or tribal structure places emphasis upon the individual's having carefully assigned responsibilities to the larger group, discouraging any imaginative deviation from these responsibilities. For deviation by the individual invites only censure from the group if he fails, and rewards for others if he succeeds.

The problem of risk taking must be given special attention. Not only all the institutions discussed above, but also the very nature of his economic situation discourages the farmer from taking the risks inherent in innovation. "Nothing ventured, nothing gained" is a true adage of the human enterprise, but a dangerous principle for the farmer in an underdeveloped country. Living as he does at the very margin of subsistence, what he ventures is different in kind from what he might hope to gain. The difference between 50 and zero is much greater than that between 50 and 100—if 50 is the minimum necessary to survival. And although the greater family or tribe shields the individual from losses caused by circumstances accepted as beyond his control, it does not normally do so for losses caused by his playing with new and therefore unsanctioned ideas.

Thus, the greater family or tribal organization of society is, in the least developed countries, probably the most potent single inhibitor of the play of those incentives necessary for inducing progress.

Institutional Factors Which Inhibit the Development of Capabilities of Rural People

As stated earlier, development appears to depend primarily upon the development of human resources and capabilities. Several of the subsequent papers will deal with the relation of education to development, and I shall touch upon it briefly later. Here, however, we are interested in another factor affecting the development of human capabilities; namely, the opportunity for individuals to acquire meaningful experience while they are young enough to try new ideas and to learn from this experience. Our society deliberately provides children with opportunities for developing self-reliance, to prepare them for their self-determining roles as young adults. This is not true in most underdeveloped countries; decision making is restricted to family elders long after the offspring have reached full adulthood. Even such decisions as whom and when to marry, what vocation to follow, how to spend their earnings, and the like, are made for, not by, the young and even the middle-aged adult. Also, in our rural society the family farm system of agriculture develops entrepreneurial and management skills, by requiring every farmer to think and act for himself, rewarding him for his good judgments, penalizing him for his mistakes. Most other systems of land tenure do not provide this built-in device of self-education. This may well be a fatal weakness, in the long run, of the collective or cooperative farm, or other modern forms of group tenure. They may be responsive in the short run to the introduction of new knowledge and technology, but they so limit the numbers of people who acquire managerial and entrepreneurial skills that, in time, they become rigid and sterile of new development potential.

Institutional Factors Which Inhibit the Development and Utilization of Science and Technology

I shall close with a few comments on the institutional factors surrounding the development and utilization of scientific knowledge and technology in the agriculture of a typical underdeveloped country.

First, we glance at the *extension and service* institutions which carry science and technology to farmers. In great part, as in our own country, this function, as well as research and education, must be carried out in the so-called "public sector." This point is seen to be important when we recognize that in the underdeveloped countries government has been evolved largely for the purpose of maintaining order and collecting revenue. Although this is most apparent in a colonial system, it is inherent even in a politically independent country to the extent that that country has pursued static rather than dynamic ends. As such countries begin actively to pursue progress as a central goal of policy, an entirely new role is demanded of government and of public service. Rural development, as distinct from the mere maintenance of order in rural areas, requires not only that public officials have technical rather than merely administrative competence, it requires that they assume a servant rather than a master relationship to the farm people with whom they work. This is a difficult transition to make, especially since in these societies the deepest cultural values inhere in status relationships. But a democratically oriented, progressive agriculture appears to require a complex system of government *services* to farmers—research service, extension service, credit service, marketing service, price-supporting service, and so on. And although names of these functions can be changed, the fundamental *service* relation between the public agent and the individual farmer is probably essential to development. At least, this is my hypothesis, as any other system, based upon authority rather than upon enlisting the informed self-interest of the farmer, has never appeared to work well anywhere. It simply requires too much overhead.

Institutions of formal education and research which have been developed during the essentially static past of the typical underdeveloped country must also make profound adaptations to their new roles as participants in the development process. Listed below are some of the more basic changes which will commonly be required.

In *research,* a change of attitude as to the basic purpose is required, anchoring it solidly in the development needs of the country's agriculture, rather than treating it as an end in itself. This requires more than a recitation of the right words. It must lead to careful analysis in selection of research problems. For the numbers of problems are legion, and the research resources and competences extremely limited. Selection of problems for research must be based on criteria such as relative importance to development, probability that research may find a solution, probable usability of the solution by farmers, and probable cost of the research. The present criterion, namely the probability of publication in a prestigious foreign journal, must give way to those of relevance.

For research to participate in agricultural development there must be new administrative and scientific alignments, a breaking down of barriers which separate related scientific disciplines, in order to reflect the analytical requirements of the problems needing solution. In most underdeveloped countries now, effective research on animal production, for example, is almost impossible because of the administrative and scientific separation of animal husbandry from crop production. Similar barriers, almost as high and impenetrable, separate soils from crop production, forestry from soil conservation—and economics from almost everything relevant to farming.

The new orientation of research toward development objectives will require much closer relationships with *extension and educational efforts*. And, especially, extension efforts must be anchored much more in such processes as exist, or can be stimulated, through which farm groups can make their wishes known. Much too commonly research findings are shot out at farmers from the research bastions, through a top-down administrative bureaucracy called Agricultural Extension or Community Development. Much more effective means of farmer participation, and indeed control—which is the real heart of our own extension system—must be evolved if research and extension are to become truly at one with the agricultural development process.

The *agricultural colleges* will also undergo substantial change as they adapt themselves to developmentary roles. The subject matter of courses will be based upon local research and experience, rather than material from foreign sources. Teaching methods will adjust to emphasize the creative use of science to achieve specific rural development objectives, rather than rote memory of scientific principles unrelated to practice. Examinations and other student appraisal devices will be modified to identify potential agricultural development capabilities of students; and faculty will be promoted in accordance with their performance.

One could go on indefinitely; the task of institutional development is not simple. But though the task is huge, we cannot be pessimistic. The margin for potential improvement is great. National annual growth rates in agricultural productivity of 6 to 8 per cent are rare; and yet in virtually all underdeveloped countries the best farmers get three or four times as much production as the average farmer from the same basic resources.

Agricultural scientists and administrators in the United States can, through their advice and example, contribute importantly to the effectiveness of the institutions for agricultural science, technology, and service in the developing countries. They are, in fact, already doing so. They will be effective, however, only in so far as they come deeply to understand the changing role which the institutions must play as the country they serve sets its course toward development. For those Americans who are privileged to participate in the process, as for all who really care what happens to mankind, it is one of this generation's most exciting tasks.

Animal Agriculture in the Emerging Nations

RALPH W. PHILLIPS

Director, International Organizations Staff, Office of the Assistant Secretary for International Affairs, United States Department of Agriculture, Washington, D. C.

THE WORLD'S BARNYARD has in it some six billion animals. How does one characterize such a large barnyard, or even that portion of it which lies in the emerging countries?

At the risk of oversimplifying a very complex subject, I have set down the following main features of animal agriculture in the emerging countries, with which I shall deal in turn:

1. Animal agriculture is practiced in many, diverse forms, so a major characteristic is its variability.

2. On the whole, the emerging countries are well stocked in terms of animal numbers.

3. Animals produce much of the draft power that is essential to plant agriculture.

4. On the other hand, the contributions of livestock and poultry to animal protein supplies are very low, either in comparison with levels of production in developed countries, or in relation to the needs of people in the emerging countries.

5. In many countries, animal and plant agriculture are not well integrated.

6. Neither the art of animal production nor animal science is well developed in most of the emerging countries.

7. The development of animal production is further handicapped in most emerging nations by the lack of adequate processing and marketing facilities.

8. Religious beliefs and social customs that inhibit the efficient production of animals and the use of animal products are further deterrents to development of the animal industries in many emerging countries, and low economic levels are a deterrent in most of them.

9. Population density is already a serious deterrent to increased animal production in many emerging countries, and rapid upswings in population numbers are further enhancing the difficulties; hence there is strong competition from food crops for the use of arable land—a competition that seems certain to grow stronger as the population upsurge continues.

10. Leaders in animal science are few, and institutions are not yet available in the emerging countries to train an adequate corps of such workers.

Before commenting briefly on each of these ten characteristics, I should add a word regarding the world's barnyard as a whole. In 1961 there were 3,042,100,000 head of cattle, water buffaloes, sheep, goats, pigs, horses, donkeys, mules, and camels (FAO, 1962a). Data for poultry are less precise, but it is estimated (Phillips, 1962) that chickens, ducks, geese, and turkeys numbered a bit over 3 billion. There are also limited numbers of other domesticated animals such as reindeer, yaks, llamas, alpacas, and guinea hens that are not included in these totals. Thus, for each of the world's people in 1961 there were approximately two domestic animals: one head of livestock and one of poultry.

Also in 1961 there were, for each of the world's 3,078,000,000 people, 0.46 hectare (1.15 acres) of arable land and land in permanent crops, and 0.84 hectare (2.07 acres) of permanent meadows and pastures. These were the areas available, on the average, upon which to grow food for each person and feed for the livestock and poultry that served each person.

MAJOR CHARACTERISTICS OF ANIMAL AGRICULTURE IN THE EMERGING COUNTRIES

Variations in Animal Agriculture

Like all things biological, animal agriculture is characterized by variability. In fact, it is extremely variable owing to the many geographic, climatic, biological, economic, sociological, and managerial factors which affect it.

Consider the ways in which these factors have interacted to result in the highly productive dairy lands of Wisconsin or the well watered, efficiently operated dairy farms of the Netherlands, as compared with milk production by yaks in the cold highlands of Tibet, or by water buffaloes in the hot, humid lowlands of India. Or, consider beef production under the conditions of good feeding that prevail on an Iowa farm or on the pampas of Argentina, as compared with that in the cool, damp highlands of Scotland, or the hot, relatively dry back country of south central Brazil. Conditions under which sheep are grazed are very different in the semi-arid country of North Africa and the Near East from those in the well watered, well managed pastures of New Zealand, or the high summer ranges in the Rocky Mountains and other western uplands of the United States. The zebu bullock pulls his load on the hot plains of India under conditions that are quite different from those under which his Simmenthal cousin provides draft power on a cool mountain farm in Switzerland, or from those under which camels carry freight through the passes of the Hindu Kush or llamas do their master's bidding in the Andean highlands.

Let us look a bit farther into the nature and extent of these variations in animal agriculture, using such statistical measures as are readily at hand.

In Fig. 1 there are set out some comparisons based on variations in land use in relation to the size of the human population. The seven regions shown are the standard ones used by the Food and Agriculture Organization. They omit the U.S.S.R. and mainland China. North America includes only Canada and the United States, plus Bermuda, Greenland, St. Pierre, and Miquelon.

In the developed and developing areas, as summarized in the two sets of columns at the right, it will be seen that in each of these areas there is about twice as much grassland (1.25 and 0.82 hectare, respectively) as there is arable land (0.64 and 0.46 hectare, respectively). However, in the developed area there is about 50 per cent more land of each type per person than in the developing area of the world. But there are marked differences within the developed area and within the developing area. Europe, for example, has only 0.36 hectare of arable land per person, as compared with 1.91 in Oceania, and Europe has a mere 0.18 hectare of grassland as compared with 27.9 hectares per person in Oceania. Differences within the developing area of the world are less pronounced. However, the crowded Far East has only 0.29 hectare of arable land

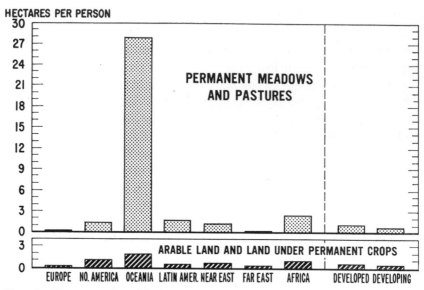

Fig. 1. Hectares of arable land and grassland per person in each of the major regions of the world, and in the developed (Europe, North America, Oceania) and developing (Latin America, Near East, Far East, Africa) areas. Data are not included for the U.S.S.R. or mainland China. North America includes Canada, the United States, Bermuda, Greenland, St. Pierre, and Miquelon.

and 0.11 of grassland per person, as compared with 1.05 hectares of arable and 2.56 hectares of grassland per person in Africa.

Such statistical measures must, of course, be used advisedly. A hectare of well watered pasture in Finland is a very different thing from a hectare of dry grazing land in Kenya. Also, within a region such as Oceania there is a great difference between the carrying capacity of a hectare of well watered, fertilized New Zealand pasture and a hectare of the dry Out Back country in Australia, or between a hectare of well managed forage on the well watered part of Fiji and a hectare of burned-over pasture in New Caledonia. Within our own country a hectare of Minnesota's dairy farming section is quite a different thing from a hectare of grazing land in the subtropical beef-producing sections of the Gulf Coast, or a hectare of semiarid grazing land in Arizona or New Mexico. The dry grazing land of Libya is a very different thing from an irrigated field of berseem in the Nile Valley in the United Arab Republic, or from a naturally well watered mountain valley in Austria.

In Fig. 2 there is set out another statistical approach to show variations in the manner in which livestock fit into the over-all pattern of agriculture. Again, the FAO regions are used, and the U.S.S.R. and mainland China are omitted. The numbers of animals, excluding poultry, are related to the number of people and to the areas of arable land and grassland in each region, and in the broad areas classified as developed and developing.

The numbers of animals per person vary from 0.52 in the densely populated Far East to 14.12 in Oceania. Numbers of animals per hectare of arable land vary from 0.93 in North America to 7.38 in Oceania. Numbers of animals per hectare of grassland vary from lows of 0.51 in Oceania and 0.61 in Africa, where extensive grazing is the widespread practice, to 4.84 in the Far East and 5.13 in Europe, where intensive farming is the rule. Here, too, one must

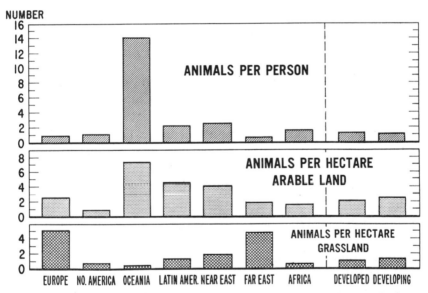

Fig. 2. Animals (cattle, water buffaloes, sheep, goats, pigs, horses, donkeys, mules, and camels) per person and per hectare of arable land and grassland in each of the major regions of the world, and in the developed (Europe, North America, Oceania) and developing (Latin America, Near East, Far East, Africa) areas. Data are not included for the U.S.S.R. or mainland China. North America includes Canada, the United States, Bermuda, Greenland, St. Pierre, and Miquelon.

accept the statistical measures cautiously, for the productivity per hectare of grazed land in Oceania is substantially higher than in Africa, and animals are fitted into the pattern of agriculture in a very different manner in Europe from that in the Far East.

Density of Stocking in the Developed and Developing Areas

If one examines only the right-hand part of Fig. 2, where the developed and developing areas of the world are compared, one does not gain the impression of extreme differences between the two. The developed portion of the world has 1.28 animals per person, as compared with 1.09 in the developing area. The density of the livestock population per unit of land is actually higher in the developing than in the developed area: 2.39 animals per hectare of arable land as compared with 2.01, and 1.34 per hectare of grassland as compared with 1.02, in the developing and developed areas, respectively.

Contributions of Animals to Draft Power on Farms

Plant agriculture in most of the emerging countries is highly dependent upon animal power. Lord Linlithgow, when he was viceroy of pre-partition India, observed that "the cow and the working bullock bear on their patient backs the whole structure of Indian agriculture." Although the tractor is finding an increasingly important place in land-clearing and leveling operations, and to some extent is being used in individual farm operations in developing countries, what was true of pre-partition India is still true of India and Pakistan and of many other countries in the Far East, the Near East, Africa, and Latin America. Animal draft power also remains an important factor in many European, and particularly southern European, countries. No data appear to have been tabulated since an FAO study was issued in 1950 (Acock, 1950). At that time it was estimated that 86.4 per cent of the draft power for agriculture in the world was supplied by animals. In the less developed regions—the Far East, Latin America, the Near East, and Africa—the percentage ranged from 99.9 to 98.3, while in continental Europe it was estimated that 85.6 per cent of the draft power was still provided by animals. In other regions the percentages were: U.S.S.R., 78.7; Oceania, 62.5; North America, 24.5; and United Kingdom, 22.7. Although there has been a continuing trend toward mechanization since the foregoing figures were compiled, changes have been most substantial in the developed areas, and the impact of tractor power is still relatively small in most of the developing countries. In fact, in many of the latter, man is still a more important competitor of the draft animal, in the supplying of power on the farm, than is the tractor.

Variations in Ability of Animals to Meet Human Needs for Animal Protein

The difference between animal agriculture in the developed areas and that in the developing areas lies primarily in the kinds of animals, and in the ways in which they are utilized—in the kinds and amounts of products harvested for human use.

This difference is reflected in part in Fig. 3, which shows the amounts of total protein and animal protein in the food supplies of 46 countries. This is an updated version of a chart I have used on other occasions (Phillips, 1963a, 1963c) and is based on data recently available from FAO (1962a).

Looking first at total protein, it will be seen that the range is from 110 grams per person per day in New Zealand to 41 grams in Surinam. In turn, the range in animal protein supplies is from 75 grams per person per day in New Zealand to 6 in India (no. 38 in Fig. 3). Of the 46 countries, 26 fall below 30 grams of animal protein. They are, from left to right, Yugoslavia (no. 5), Greece (no. 6), Turkey (no. 13), Rhodesia and Nyasaland (no. 20), Italy (no. 23), Syria, Chile, Spain (nos. 25–27), and (beginning with no. 29) U.A.R., Portugal, Japan, Mexico, Paraguay, Brazil, Venezuela, China (Taiwan), Ecuador, India, Libya, Peru, the Philippines, Colombia, Pakistan, Ceylon, Mauritius, and Surinam.

It will be recognized that, with the exception of Japan and five southern European countries where climatic and other factors contribute to generally low economic levels, these countries fall within the major regions that are classified as underdeveloped. Among the 26 countries listed, it should be noted that Yugoslavia (no. 5),

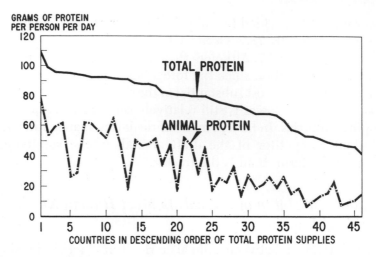

GRAMS OF PROTEIN
PER PERSON PER DAY

COUNTRIES IN DESCENDING ORDER OF TOTAL PROTEIN SUPPLIES

FIG. 3. Variations in total protein and animal protein supplies in 46 countries, based on FAO (1962*a*) data. Countries, arranged from left to right in descending order of total protein supplies, are identified by numbers as follows: 1, New Zealand; 2, France; 3, Ireland; 4, Uruguay; 5, Yugoslavia; 6, Greece; 7, Canada; 8, Australia; 9, Denmark; 10, Finland; 11, United States; 12, Argentina; 13, Turkey; 14, Switzerland; 15, Austria; 16, Belgium/Luxembourg; 17, United Kingdom; 18, Israel; 19, Norway; 20, Rhodesia and Nyasaland; 21, Sweden; 22, Federal Republic of Germany; 23, Italy; 24, Netherlands; 25, Syria; 26, Chile; 27, Spain; 28, South Africa; 29, U.A.R.; 30, Portugal; 31, Japan; 32, Mexico; 33, Paraguay; 34, Brazil; 35, Venezuela; 36, China (Taiwan); 37, Ecuador; 38, India; 39, Libya; 40, Peru; 41, Philippines; 42, Colombia; 43, Pakistan; 44, Ceylon; 45, Mauritius; 46, Surinam.

Greece (no. 6), Turkey (no. 13), Rhodesia and Nyasaland (no. 20), and Italy (no. 23) have 80 or more grams of total protein per person; in other words, these countries have developed cropping systems whereby they produce relatively large amounts of proteins from plant sources, thus offsetting at least in part the shortage of animal proteins. On the other hand, among the 20 countries having 30 or more grams of animal protein per person per day, there are 2 that are usually classified as less developed: Uruguay (no. 4) and Argentina (no. 12). Pastoral agriculture dominates the scene in both these countries, and both are traditionally large consumers of meat.

If we look now at Fig. 4, where the same 46 countries are ar-

M'Bororo cattle eke out a poor existence on hot, dry range land in the Sudan

Boran cattle on dry but well managed, productive range in Kenya

Animals, such as these water buffaloes in Pakistan, still provide much of the power on farms and for the movement of farm products to market. (*FAO photo*)

In the dry country of the Near East, fat-tailed milking sheep such as this Awassi ewe in Israel make important contributions to the animal protein supply.

Although many useful types of livestock and poultry are found in the emerging nations, programs for genetic improvement are few. Some of the more impressive types, such as this Kankrej bull in India, have been developed for draft purposes.

In many areas, adequate levels of nutrition probably cannot be attained unless animal products are supplemented by proteins from other sources such as the pulses, and from fisheries. (*FAO photo*)

Improved livestock management and the control of animal diseases and parasites are essential if man's needs for animal products are to be met in the emerging countries. Here, an animal is vaccinated against rinderpest in Afghanistan. (*FAO photo*)

A simple cheese-making technique that has been introduced in Nepal. After being squeezed into a kind of noodle, the cheese is spread on bamboo mats or on roofs to dry. (*Photo by E. Siegenthaler*)

Small farm flocks of poultry, such as these chickens and a goose in central China, make important contributions to animal protein supplies, and could be utilized much more fully in many areas.

ranged from left to right in descending order of the Calories available per person per day, it will be seen that the range is from 3570 Calories in Ireland to 1810 in Surinam. It will also be seen that, in general, those countries that are lowest in availability of Calories are also low in both total protein and animal protein supplies. All the 17 countries beginning with Paraguay (no. 30) that have 2500 or fewer Calories have 70 grams or less of total protein, with the exception of Syria (no. 35), which, like some other countries already mentioned, draws a large portion of its protein supplies from plant sources. Before leaving Fig. 4, it is worth noting that 16 countries fall below a 20-gram level in animal protein supplies—the range is 6 to 19 grams—and the countries are Turkey (no. 21), Brazil, Rhodesia and Nyasaland (nos. 25, 26), U.A.R. (no. 29),

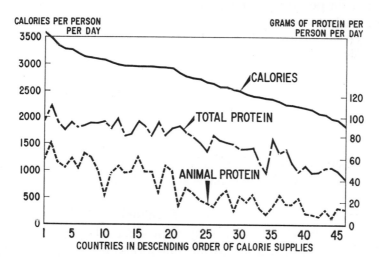

Fig. 4. Variations in calorie, total protein, and animal protein supplies in 46 countries, based on FAO (1962a) data. Countries, arranged from left to right in descending order of calorie supplies, are identified by numbers as follows: 1, Ireland; 2, New Zealand; 3, Denmark; 4, United Kingdom; 5, Australia; 6, Switzerland; 7, United States; 8, Canada; 9, Finland; 10, Yugoslavia; 11, Austria; 12, France; 13, Netherlands; 14, Norway; 15, Uruguay; 16, Argentina; 17, Federal Republic of Germany; 18, Greece; 19, Sweden; 20, Belgium/Luxembourg; 21, Turkey; 22, Israel; 23, Italy; 24, Spain; 25, Brazil; 26, Rhodesia and Nyasaland; 27, Chile; 28, South Africa; 29, U.A.R.; 30, Paraguay; 31, Mexico; 32, Portugal; 33, China (Taiwan); 34, Mauritius; 35, Syria; 36, Venezuela; 37, Japan; 38, Ecuador; 39, Colombia; 40, Libya; 41, Ceylon; 42, Pakistan; 43, Peru; 44, India; 45, Philippines; 46, Surinam.

China (Taiwan), Mauritius, Syria (nos. 33–35), Japan, Ecuador (nos. 37, 38), and (from no. 40 on) Libya, Ceylon, Pakistan, Peru, India, the Philippines, and Surinam.

The differences in levels of animal protein supplies are, to a substantial degree, but a reflection of the levels of production of specific animal products in relation to the size of the human population. Let me cite just a few figures from an earlier paper (Phillips, 1963a) to illustrate the point.

New Zealand produces about 221 pounds of beef and veal per person per year, as compared with 2.5 in the Far East.

The United States produces about 58 pounds of pork per person per year, as compared with 2.5 pounds in the Far East.

New Zealand produces about 400 pounds of mutton and lamb per person per year, as compared with only about 1.2 pounds in the Far East.

The total meat supply from bovines, swine, sheep, and goats in the Far East adds up to only about 6.2 pounds per person per year.

Eggs, too, are in short supply in many less developed countries. Here in the United States we harvest about 44.2 pounds of hens' eggs per person per year, as compared with only 2.3 pounds in the Far East.

New Zealand harvests about 4953 pounds of milk, Denmark 2454 pounds, and the Netherlands 1273 pounds per person per year, as compared with an annual harvest of only 71 pounds in the Far East.

Thus, a major characteristic of animal agriculture in many emerging countries is its inability to produce adequate amounts of animal protein in relation to the nutritional needs of the people.

Insufficient Integration of Crop and Animal Agriculture

It is hardly possible to discuss animal agriculture without some reference to the whole of agriculture of which it is a part.

Failure to recognize the value of a coordinated approach to crop and animal husbandry appeared early in man's history. In the fourth chapter of Genesis it is recorded that Cain, a tiller of the soil, slew Abel, a keeper of sheep, because Abel's offering found greater favor. In northern and northwest China it was said that "when the fields reach the hilltop, the turban comes over." and a Great Wall was built to keep two economies and two civilizations apart. This type of struggle still continues, for example, between the nomadic pastoral tribesmen and the settled farmers in parts of the Near East. In an uncrowded world man could perhaps afford the luxury of such conflict, but, looking to the future, an integrated approach is essential if man's ever-increasing needs for food are to be met, in respect both to quantity and to quality, from an efficient, balanced agriculture.

It need hardly be added that I do not subscribe to the view held in some parts of the world, and particularly in some of the emerging countries, that animal science and husbandry is something apart from agriculture and that it is a subject-matter area to be treated as a pawn over which agronomists and veterinarians struggle for control.

Lack of Development of the Art and Science of Animal Production in the Emerging Countries

The low levels of livestock products available in relation to human needs in the emerging countries may be attributed in part to a number of factors that relate to climate, to the genetic makeup of livestock and poultry, to the feed supply, and to managerial factors including animal health.

Climatic conditions in many of the emerging countries are generally unfavorable to efficient livestock production, as compared with conditions in the developed countries, which, for the most part, lie in the temperate zones. Many of the emerging countries lie between the Tropic of Cancer and the Tropic of Capricorn. Hence, the animals maintained in these countries are subjected to the debilitating effects of the hot tropics, whether the weather pattern be that of the wet tropics, or the alternating wet and dry of the monsoonal areas, or the semiarid conditions that prevail in some tropical areas. In addition to the direct effects of hot weather upon the animals, livestock are also subject to its indirect effects upon the feed supply, which in the tropics is generally coarse when rainfall is adequate, and coarse and dry when it is not. Also, whereas hot climates tend to affect animals adversely, they are generally favorable to the development of parasites that prey upon livestock and poultry.

Limitations are also imposed by climate on animal production in semiarid regions outside the tropics, in high altitudes whether within or outside the tropics, and, of course, in the far north or south. The less developed countries of North Africa and the Near East are among those that face the rigors of a climate that is generally semiarid, and in some parts arid. Southern and south-eastern European countries experience the dry summers that typify the Mediterranean climate, and consequently hover in an uncertain status between developing and developed. Areas such as the high Andes, and the Himalayas and their western extension, the Hindu Kush, are adversely affected by short grazing seasons, and by long, cold winters for which feed must be stored or during which animals must forage for a living on dried grass, which often must be searched for under snow. Low rainfall in some of these high areas adds to the difficulty of practicing productive animal husbandry.

Efforts at genetic improvement of livestock and poultry have centered largely in the developed countries of the temperate zones. In these countries, adequate feed supplies, generally adequate control of diseases and parasites, and economic capacity of the people to absorb the products of genetically improved animals have led to substantial efforts to increase the inherent productive capacities of livestock and poultry. Conversely, these stimuli usually have not been present in the less developed areas, and often the main requirement of an animal has been ability to survive. Although government stations and limited numbers of individuals have made some efforts to improve the local animals, substantial efforts by large groups of breeders have been lacking, and the livestock and poultry found in the emerging countries are, for the most part, not specialized for meat, milk, wool, or egg production. Many distinct local types and breeds have emerged, owing to geographic isolation, to interest of a local leader in a particular color or type, or to other circumstances, but levels of productivity, particularly of milk, wool, and eggs, remain low. Perhaps the most specialized types are found among the breeds of cattle which have evolved primarily as draft animals to provide the essential power on farms.

Low animal productivity in the emerging countries results also from inadequate quality and quantity of feed supplies, to which reference has already been made. The farmer whose very existence depends upon the pair of bullocks or other draft animals that provide power for his plow will generally find the best feed he can for those animals. But when the main roughage is rice or wheat straw, when the kitchen stove is an important competitor for that straw, and when pressure on the arable land is such that most or all of it must be used for the production of human food, then even the working bullock must often exist on short rations. The few chickens or other poultry, and such other livestock as may be kept on a small farm, usually must scavenge for much of their feed. Where grazing on open range is practiced, the very young or the very old people move out from villages with the animals during the day and bring them back at night, or nomadic groups "follow the grass" as the seasons change. Production of forage or other feed specifically for livestock is generally not a part of the crop rotation system. In any event, high-protein forage crops are generally lacking in the tropics. Storage of hay for the winter feeding of livestock is almost an unknown practice in many areas. Integration of nomadic livestock production and settled farming operations is yet to be achieved in some parts of the world. Here, it must be remembered that most emerging countries do not have the equivalent of our corn belt through which to pass cattle and sheep for fattening en route from the open range to the main centers of consumption. A specialized dairy industry is developing around Bombay and some other cities in India. Specialized poultry farms are emerging in Thailand and some other countries of southeastern Asia. But such operations are the exception rather than the rule in these and other emerging countries.

I have already touched upon some aspects of animal management, and the subject is far too complicated to do more than mention it here. However, a few points should be added. Range and pasture management have been the subjects of intensive research, and adoption of improved practices has been widespread, in the developed countries. But in the emerging countries, such developments may be found only in isolated instances. Moreover, good husbandry practices, aimed at protection of animals from adverse climates, at ensuring adequate care at critical times such as calving and lambing, at the prevention of parasitic infections, and at fitting efficient animal production into an over-all pattern of balanced agriculture, have not evolved to a high degree in the emerging countries. Also, these countries are still the main reservoirs of infection of such killing and debilitating diseases as rinderpest and foot-and-mouth disease.

Lack of Adequate Processing and Marketing Facilities

Another major deterrent to efficient animal production in many emerging countries is the lack of adequate processing and marketing facilities. Slaughtering facilities are often very primitive. Inadequate care of fresh hides and skins in many areas leads to deterioration and substantial economic loss. Lack of transport often requires the movement of animals on foot over long distances to market. Lack of refrigeration makes it necessary to utilize meat quickly and near the point of slaughter, and milk and eggs near the points of production. Inspection as a safeguard to human health may be inadequate; often it is entirely lacking. Neither are there facilities for adequate utilization of the by-products of the packing industry. A prosperous animal industry can hardly be expected to develop in a country where the essential links—processing and marketing facilities—between the producer and the consumer are too weak to meet the needs of either group.

Adverse Effects of Religious Beliefs, Social Customs, and Economic Levels on Efficient Animal Production

The difficulties are further enhanced in those countries where religious beliefs and social customs place limitations on the development of efficient animal production. Pigs, which are one of the more efficient converters of feed into meat, have no place in a Moslem society. In predominantly Hindu India, with its 18.8 per cent or nearly one-fifth of the world's cattle, and just over half the world's water buffaloes, most of the people avoid the eating of beef on religious grounds. The tribesman of Africa or the Near East, who measures his wealth in animal numbers rather than in terms of what he harvests from them, makes little use of processing and marketing facilities, no matter how modern they may be, and it is difficult to convince him of the advisability of limiting numbers in the interest of improved range management.

Also among the deterrents to efficient animal production in the emerging countries is the low average economic level of the people in all these countries. Whether the population be dense or relatively sparse, animal products are generally expensive as compared with food from plant sources, and when per capita incomes are less than $100 per year, as they are in many of the emerging countries, the demand for animal products is limited, and consequently the incentive to production that results from increased demand is also limited.

Competition for the Use of Land

In the densely populated countries, crops that produce food for direct human consumption occupy most of the arable land. Bullocks, water buffaloes, or other draft animals will usually be kept to till the fields. A pig may be fattened, mostly on refuse. A goat may graze on the dikes between rice fields. A few chickens, ducks, or geese may scavenge for food. But otherwise the farm is devoted primarily to plant agriculture.

Granted that all human needs for protein in the years ahead can hardly be met from livestock and poultry sources, two other lines of development are being explored by some countries: (a) greater use of fish, both from ponds and from marine fisheries, and (b) greater use of proteins from plant sources. As noted earlier, some of the less developed countries have already made substantial progress in the direction of producing protein supplies from plant sources.

Lack of Technical and Scientific Leadership

Another feature of animal agriculture in the emerging countries is the great dearth of trained leaders to guide its improvement. Institutions where such leaders could acquire training have, for the most part, been built in the temperate zones, in the economically well developed countries. Developing countries have been limited in the numbers of trainees they could send to such institutions. When trainees did come, the training they received was often limited in its applicability to the less developed countries.

Now, many newly independent countries find themselves with few and sometimes no trained men in the field of animal science. Of the few that are available, most have been trained in veterinary medicine, rather than in animal breeding, feeding, or management, and in any event their task in controlling animal diseases and parasites is so large that they have little time for the art and science of animal production.

Moreover, leaders in the newly emerging countries are faced with the immediate problems of meeting the needs of rapidly increasing populations for food, and they naturally turn to the main sources of Calories, and to increased use of improved varieties of plants, fertilizers, and pesticides. Thus, attempts to bolster supplies of animal protein either are left to one side or are assigned relatively low priorities, as is also the training of leaders who might spearhead future efforts to improve animal production.

SOME POSSIBILITIES FOR IMPROVEMENT

All this is not to say that no improvement can be brought about. Quite the contrary is true, in spite of all the difficulties to be overcome. In fact, the rapid rise that is taking place in the human population, though it makes more difficult the achievement of adequate levels of production of animal products, makes more urgent the finding of satisfactory solutions.

In so far as solutions lie in the greater output of animal products, the main avenues of approach will probably be:

Development of crop rotation systems, in intensively cultivated areas, that contribute both to the maintenance of high levels of soil fertility and to feed supplies for animals kept as adjuncts to plant agriculture.

Greater use of the more efficient converters of feed, such as dairy cattle, pigs, and poultry, where feed supplies permit, including the development of small production units in intensely cropped areas.

Development of more productive types, particularly of beef cattle and sheep, for extensive grazing areas; adoption of efficient range management practices; and development of supplemental sources of feed for use during droughts or seasonal periods of short range-feed supply.

Improvement of veterinary services, and management practices that contribute to disease and parasite control.

Exploration of ways of using relatively rough lands, that are currently lying idle or are of little economic use in the emerging countries, for livestock production.

Continuation of the search for types of animals, or development of new types, so as best to meet the specific requirements imposed by the many varied environments under which livestock and poultry are produced (Phillips, 1948, 1961).

Shifting patterns of production in order that there may be greater concentration upon the production of food crops in areas adapted to intensive crop production, coupled with greater emphasis on animal production in areas better suited to mixed farming. Such shifts have been taking place in recent times within the United States (Durost and Barton, 1960). They may be expected to take place within other countries, and, tariff walls permitting, between countries.

Development of improved transportation, processing, and marketing facilities in order to provide adequate links between producers and consumers within the emerging countries, or between producers and export facilities, where the animal industries of emerging countries yield animal products surplus to their own needs.

Supplementing inadequate supplies of animal protein with proteins from pulses and other plant sources and, where feasible, from fisheries.

Training the corps of workers that are essential at the research, extension, and other levels if such programs are to be evolved and implemented in the emerging countries.

CONCLUSION

This treatment of the world's barnyard, with particular attention to that large portion of it which lies in the emerging countries, has been brief indeed, in relation to the size and complexity of the subject. Ten of the major characteristics of animal agriculture in the emerging countries are discussed. There are also set out a few of the avenues of approach that seem likely to yield the greatest returns in balanced agricultural production and better human nutrition. Although there are substantial opportunities for increasing the output of animal products in the emerging countries, there are major difficulties to be overcome. Unless there are vastly increased efforts on many fronts, however, it will be difficult even to maintain present per capita levels of production and consumption (Phillips, 1963b, 1963c).

REFERENCES

ACOCK, A. M. 1950. *Progress and Economic Problems in Farm Mechanization.* Food and Agriculture Organization of the United Nations, Rome.

DUROST, DONALD D., and GLEN T. BARTON. 1960. *Changing Sources of Farm Output.* ARS Production Research Report No. 36, U. S. Department of Agriculture, Washington, D. C.

FAO. 1962a. *Production Yearbook, 1962.* Vol. 16. Food and Agriculture Organization of the United Nations, Rome.

FAO. 1962b. *The State of Food and Agriculture, 1962.* Food and Agriculture Organization of the United Nations, Rome.

PHILLIPS, RALPH W. 1948. *Breeding Livestock Adapted to Unfavorable Environments.* Agriculture Study No. 1, Food and Agriculture Organization of the United Nations, Rome.

PHILLIPS, RALPH W. 1961. Untapped sources of animal germ plasm. In *Germ Plasm Resources* (Ralph E. Hodgson, editor), pp. 43–75. American Association for the Advancement of Science, Washington, D. C.

PHILLIPS, RALPH W. 1962. The livestock industry—Its scope and potential. In *Introduction to Livestock Production* (H. H. Cole, editor), chap. 1, pp. 1–25. W. H. Freeman and Co., San Francisco.

PHILLIPS, RALPH W. 1963a. Animal products in the diets of present and future world populations. *J. Animal Sci., 22,* 251–262.

PHILLIPS, RALPH W. 1963b. *Summary of Proceedings on Agriculture of the United Nations Conference on the Application of Science and Technology for the Benefit of the Less Developed Areas.* FAO World Food Congress Background Paper WFC/63/BP/UNCSAT, Food and Agriculture Organization of the United Nations, Rome.

PHILLIPS, RALPH W. 1963c. The necessity of defining needs and establishing priorities for solution of animal production problems, taking into consideration the needs of human nutrition. In *Efficiency of Animal Production* (Proceedings, World Conference on Animal Production), Vol. 1, *Main Reports,* pp. 7–45. European Association for Animal Production, Rome.

Plant Agriculture in the Emerging Nations

J. B. PETERSON

Head, Department of Agronomy, Purdue University, Lafayette, Indiana

R. D. FRAZIER

Graduate Research Assistant, Department of Agronomy, Purdue University, Lafayette, Indiana; formerly Agronomist, Purdue-Brazil Project

PLANT AGRICULTURE has been changing rapidly in the past few years. The nature of these changes has varied with natural geographic areas and with political units. The interaction of environment with man's activity on plant agriculture over time has been great. Its dimensions are so great as to be obvious even though the data available are often based on estimates.

REGIONAL DIFFERENCES IN FOOD PRODUCTION IN GENERAL

Although world food production, which except for marine life depends on the production of land plants, has risen steadily in the past five years, there has apparently been little change in world food production per caput (FAO, 1963, p. 16). This is the result of a corresponding increase in world population. The main increase in per caput production since World War II has been in Europe and North America, rather than in the less developed regions, with the exception of the Near East, where food production per caput has stayed above the prewar level. In Africa immediately after the war, prewar levels were readily reached only to fall away; in 1961–1962 and 1962–1963 food production per head fell to levels lower than those of the prewar years. In the Far East (excluding mainland China), the world's most populous region, the prewar level of food production per caput was exceeded only in the year 1960–1961. In Latin America the prewar level was equaled only in 1958–1959. These developing regions have not fallen behind North America and Europe in total production of food. Their

33

poor showing per caput is the result of rapidly expanding populations. This is especially true of Latin America, which although it
has shown the greatest increase of any area in total postwar as
compared with prewar food production, has also had the greatest
rate of population growth.

In 1961–1962 the rate of world population increase was estimated at 1.8 per cent per year. World food production averaged
about 13 per cent more per caput than that of prewar times, the
greatest per caput increase being in the developed nations, where
the population rise was not as great as in the developing nations
(FAO, 1963, pp. 15–16). The year 1961–1962 varied in detail from
the postwar trend in that there was a brief pause in the increase
in total agricultural production, largely the result of widespread
bad weather. Agricultural production increased noticeably only in
Latin America; totals fell sharply in Africa and the Near East as
a result of droughts; production declined also in western Europe
and North America; a third successive poor crop season apparently
occurred in mainland China. These data illustrate the oscillations
that can be expected in the long-time trends of food production
over the world because of climatic variations, and demonstrate
that eventually world food supply must depend on man's capacity
to modify the effects of climatic factors.

For 1962–1963 the Food and Agriculture Organization reports
(FAO, 1963, pp. 15–16) an apparent food production increase in
each of the main regions of the world except Latin America and
the Far East. The slight fall indicated by the estimates for Latin
America apparently resulted from lowered output of coffee in
Brazil, sugar in Cuba, and winter grains in Argentina. Production
is estimated to have been up only 1 per cent in the Far East (excluding mainland China), whereas in Africa, the Near East,
Oceania, and western Europe the increase for 1962–1963 was 4 to
5 per cent. The total world agricultural production rose 2 to 3 per
cent in 1962–1963 according to FAO's preliminary estimates, thus
keeping slightly ahead of the estimated annual population growth
of 2 per cent.

Man's thinking regarding potential total world food production
is usually linked with estimates of population growth. Man remained sparsely distributed during the neolithic period (Davis,

1963, p. 63), being held back by epidemics, pillage, and disasters such as flood and drought. There was little change in the rate of increase of the earth's inhabitation by man until the sixteenth and seventeenth centuries, when the annual rate of increase doubled. The pattern of human regeneration since that time is commonly known, particularly the doubling of the world's population between 1850 and 1920 and the 1 billion increase in the 23 years since 1940. The medium projections of the United Nations give a rate for the remainder of this century which will, if continued, multiply the world's population sevenfold in 100 years. The spectacular rise in world population has not taken place uniformly. It has been highly differentiated by regions. The demographic evolution of modern nations has been largely determined by the pattern of decline of the death rate (Davis, *loc. cit.*). Death rate first began to decline in northwestern Europe. The cause of the decline is credited partly to improved living conditions, and partly to the growth of medical science and the dissemination and application of the resulting techniques for prevention and cure of disease. The relative importance of the two is debated. Because of its early demographic evolution, Europe is frequently studied to find the bases for predicting trends in the rest of the world. Most frequently noted is the reaction to rapid population growth which became quite apparent, particularly in the Scandinavian countries, early in this century. The decline of population growth in these countries may be ascribed to the heavy emigration from Europe, and to increase in birth control in spite of opposition from the church and state, and a delaying of the age of marriage. Davis (*loc. cit.*) discounts the two "popular" views that population growth is good for business and that numerical limitation comes from the threat of poverty. He gives most credit for a slowing down of population increase in developed or advanced countries to a growing desire for new opportunities which compete for family income that would otherwise be available for supporting more children. He points out that the great population increases in the underdeveloped countries bear little relation to their economic conditions. In thirty-four developing countries the correlation between population growth and economic gain during the 1950's was negligible. He believes the evidence indicates that the population upsurge in the developing countries is not helping them to grow economically. Hence, we cannot assume that increased population in itself will bring the prosperity which seems in time to generate a desire to restrict families and thus to provide a built-in governor regulating the overpopulation of the world. On the other hand, Davis believes that the agrarian peoples of the developing nations will realize a slowdown in birth rate before long, not because of poverty and deprivation, but because of awareness of the situation in the "industrialized and affluent fourth of the world."

In the meantime a close look at plant agriculture and population trends in developing nations shows that the situation has often been unique in each major region of the world and frequently in each country. The efficiency of agricultural production has grown in industrialized areas but has remained static or even declined elsewhere (Scrimshaw, 1963, p. 73). The regions of the world show marked differences in shares of the world's income, agricultural land, and agricultural production in relation to population. The Far East has half the world's population but only 15 per cent of the income. It has noticeably less agricultural land than Europe, which has less than half as many people and a more slowly increasing population. North America has approximately 40 per cent of the world's income but only a little over 10 per cent of the agricultural land. North America, Latin America, Africa, the Near East, and Oceania have higher proportions of the world's agricultural land in respect to their populations than do the Far East and Europe.

Among the most revealing indicators of the varying levels of agricultural efficiency over the world are the differences in output per adult male agricultural worker as given by FAO (Table I).

Crop yields respond with great sensitivity to soil, climate, and technology. Average yields often vary markedly from country to country, although the range in yield within certain countries is equally great. Apparently there is some coincidence between the world's political boundaries and natural ecologic boundaries. This may justify in part using country averages to demonstrate the variance in the world. Not only the variance, but also the great impact of modern technology on agricultural production is shown by the data given in Table II.

TABLE I.   Net output per adult male engaged in agriculture

(FAO, 1963, p. 117)

Country	Indices (Italy = 100)
United States	412
Canada	286
United Kingdom	256
Denmark	228
Germany, Federal Republic of	219 [a]
Israel	200 [b]
Norway	176
France	158
Italy	100
Argentina	87
Greece	66
Panama	60
Japan	54
Venezuela	47
Korea, Republic of	20
India	18 [b]
Thailand	15 [a]

[a] Gross domestic product at market prices expressed as relative to the corresponding figure for the United States.

[b] Net domestic product at factor cost expressed as relative to the corresponding figure for the United States.

TABLE II.   Percentage increase in wheat yield,
1909–1913 to 1958–1960

(FAO, 1963, p. 104)

Country	Percentage increase in yield
Mexico	282
Bulgaria	181
Argentina	89
France	83
Netherlands	78
New Zealand	75
Japan	74
United States	71
Greece	56
Denmark	30

FAO, in discussing these data, points out that large increases in yield of wheat were obtained in some countries in less than two decades. Yields of rice also reflect the influence of technology and demonstrate the relatively short time required to raise productivity by the adoption of improved methods. The current yields from the highest-yielding countries are about seven times those from the lowest-yielding countries (FAO, 1963, p. 105). Because of wide differences in the rate of increase of rice yield, the ranking of the countries today is very different from what it was before World War I. At that time the average yields of rice in the United States and China (Taiwan) were much the same as those in India and Pakistan. Since then, yields in India and Pakistan have shown no net gain, whereas those in Taiwan and the United States have risen by 80 and 120 per cent, respectively.

Such trends lead FAO to emphasize the possibility of increasing productivity per acre markedly and rapidly by bringing new technology to bear where it has not been applied before.

SPECIFIC CHARACTERISTICS OF AGRICULTURAL SYSTEMS IN EMERGING NATIONS

Anyone who has attempted to appraise the status of agriculture in the emerging nations of the world is keenly aware of the paucity of adequate data. Even the components of agricultural operations in these countries are difficult to appraise with the existing inadequate reporting systems and inadequate gathering, processing, and interpretation of data. We are particularly aware of the difficulties which members of review teams encounter when estimating the relative importance of different farming enterprises in the rapidly improving nations because of the frequent lack of adequate data-collecting and reporting programs. Perhaps the lack of good data is a common characteristic of emerging nations.

Dependence Historically on Only a Few Export Crops

The colonial pattern of settlement and development of many of the nations of the world frequently initiated a one-crop, export economy. Such an export often did not greatly benefit the workers and left the economy of the country quite vulnerable to world conditions influencing these highly specialized markets. The history of Brazil well illustrates the point.

Brazil was the first land in the New World to yield an agricultural commodity for export to the Old (Furtado, 1963, p. 209). On the heels of the miners who were finding and developing a great industry in precious metals, the Portuguese established sugar plantations on the hot and humid eastern seaboard south of the Amazon delta. Sugar production on the Cape Verdes and the Madeiras in the Atlantic had already created a market for Portuguese sugar in Europe. The Brazilian plantations were moving toward a monopoly of sugar a hundred years before the settlement of New England. For two hundred years the sugar industry flourished in a narrow 1500-mile strip along the coast, reaching inland no more than 60 miles. The sugar economy underwrote the early occupation of Brazil. From the beginning it was based on slave labor, mostly from Africa.

In the great northeastern section of Brazil, the Nordeste, the rainfall decreases rapidly a few miles from the eastern coast to less than 20 inches a year. Cattle raising developed in this region to supply draft animals for the sugar plantations and mills. A world-wide export business in leather followed. Slave labor for this industry was recruited largely from the native Indian population. As a result of the struggles for power in Europe in the seventeenth century, the Dutch came into control of the Brazilian sugar industry. The Dutch were in control for only a quarter of a century, being expelled in 1654, but they had learned the business of sugar production well enough to transfer the knowledge to the West Indies. There the competing system they established liquidated the Brazilian sugar monopoly. The Brazilian economy had been tied so tightly to sugar that it went into a long period of decline until early in the eighteenth century, when gold was discovered in the plateau region (Furtado, 1963, p. 212).

In the latter part of the eighteenth century the production of gold and diamonds declined. In the meantime the Europeans who had settled southern Brazil, particularly in São Paulo, had developed a colonial export agriculture based on coffee culture, which became well established by 1850. The ups and downs of this one-crop economy are well known. Frequent surpluses brought government intervention, culminating in the 1930's in a policy of destroying surpluses.

This story of a search for a special, profitable commodity to export to the rest of the world is also the story of many of today's developing nations. From 1530 to 1930 the Brazilian economy depended on external demand. In the three periods when the magic products sugar, gold, and coffee were in a favored world position, the economy flourished. In the interim periods there was economic stagnation.

Furtado (1963, p. 216) points out that with the decline in dependence on the export of coffee for income, the Brazilian economy is becoming more diversified and more independent, in respect both to agriculture and to industry. He reports that the substitution of home-produced consumer goods for imports was almost completed by 1957. He gives a 4.6 per cent increase in agricultural production over the past 15 years, a gain which has been largely offset by increases in population, with the result that the relative supply of agricultural goods has lessened.

Incomplete, Inconsistent, and Scattered Application of Known Technology

The adoption of agricultural technology in the emerging nations is usually spotty, so that one observes many anachronisms of oxen and tractors, hand hoeing and mechanical or even chemical weed control, hand harvesting and mechanical harvesting on adjacent farms or even in the same field. These paradoxes produce in the trained agriculturist a reaction akin to what the tourist feels while watching the mixture of ancient and modern modes of transportation in the typical traffic of many of these lands. One sees the flow of new technology along the lines of least resistance into the areas where the invitation to improve procedure is greatest. Stimulation to change must come from awareness of the benefits, understanding of the techniques, and availability of capital to implement them. In 1961 the authors saw oxen and tractors plowing the same field in Brazil. We also saw crews of men and women turning over land with the typical large Brazilian hoe in lieu of plowing, while in neighboring fields tractors were pulling two- and three-bottom plows. Several times in Chile, Peru, and Colombia, the senior author was told by farm managers that at the current prices of labor it was hard for tractors to compete with men and oxen. It was pointed out that an ox could be used for eight years and sold at a price which would replace or nearly replace him. Much of the local meat supply was said to be provided by these eight-year retired oxen. Tractor operation was faced with high prices for fuel and inadequate maintenance service, often distant from the farm a hundred miles or more.

A successful seed producer near Santiago, Chile, uses horses and a large crew of people in preference to greater mechanization which he could readily finance. His records have convinced him that it is more economical to use this cheap source of labor than to go to power-driven machines with their high cost of maintenance and the high cost of motor fuel. For those of us who were young early in the century a trip into a developing country is like taking a walk into the past, when automobiles mingled with fancy surreys, teams worked fields alongside tractors, and a popular subject of debate in agricultural colleges was the relative efficiency of horses and tractors.

Adoption of New Techniques

Probably the two most readily accepted and most commonly observed technological advances in developing lands are the use of mineral fertilizers and the introduction of improved crop varieties.

In industrialized countries fertilizers are considered so essential to the total economy that they are promoted by governments, educational institutions dealing with farmers, and industries dependent on agriculture, particularly the fertilizer industry. A similar development is beginning to appear in the emerging countries. A good beginning has been made in many countries with the technical assistance of different agencies (FAO, 1963, p. 174). Some of those which have been most active in promoting fertilizer availability and use are FAO; the International Rice Commission, an arm of the FAO, which established a fertilizer working party in 1951; the United States Agency for International Development (AID), formerly ICA; the fertilizer industry; The Rockefeller Foundation in Latin America; and The Ford Foundation's Pilot Package Project in India. It is worth noting that Japanese cooperatives have acted as official agencies for the distribution of fertilizers.

Three hundred rice experiments in mainland China showed an average increase from 2300 to 3200 kg/ha from the use of fertilizer, an increase of 39 per cent. Experiments conducted in Chile at the University of Concepción in cooperation with The Rockefeller Foundation produced 1300 kg/ha of beef per year on irrigated ladino clover with adequate applications of nitrogen, phosphorus, and potassium. East of Valdivia, Chile, 90 bushels of wheat per acre are commonly grown with applications of 300 pounds of P_2O_5 per year, necessary because of the extremely high phosphorus-fixing power of the olivine-bearing volcanic ash present in soils of the region. In the Cauca Valley, Colombia, the climate permits a two-semester crop year. At the experiment station at Tibaitata, 115 bushels of wheat and 80 metric tons of potatoes per acre can be grown the same year if adequate amounts of mineral fertilizers are used.

Quinn (Quinn *et al.*, 1961), in south central Brazil, in one of the most comprehensive and precise grazing trials ever undertaken in the world increased beef production on colonial guinea grass, as measured by grazing steers, from 301 kg/ha to 703 kg/ha by applying 200 kg N, 200 kg P_2O_5, and 60 kg S per hectare. Only nitrogen was repeated the second year. The results of these experiments would seem applicable to a huge area of Brazil, where the average beef production is much less than that reported for Quinn's check plots. The treatments mentioned gave an average annual net return of $42.46 per hectare.

Statistics on fertilizer use point up as well as any single set of data the differences in the rate of technological advance between areas of the world. They emphasize the rapid advances in the highly developed countries since the beginning of the century. From 1945–1946 to 1960–1961, world fertilizer consumption rose 280 per cent while the area of land crops increased only 20 per cent (FAO, 1963, p. 137). In the 12 years from 1949–1950 to 1960–1961 the largest net increase in consumption of all fertilizers was shown by Europe, 6,400,000 tons; North America followed with 3,450,000 tons, the Far East 2,040,000 tons, U.S.S.R. 1,300,000 tons, Latin America only 700,000 tons, and Africa and the Near East about 250,000 tons each. Obviously, until fertilizer use approaches the rates in the highly productive nations the developing nations cannot hope to produce food at equal rates per land area. No agronomist expects native fertility, even in the few land areas where it is yet naturally high, to last more than a few brief years under the demands of modern cropping systems.

Fertilizers are applied in the less developed countries much more commonly to cash crops than to basic food crops. This reflects the single-crop culture of large plantations managed by well informed people, the easier access to credit for cash-crop farmers, and the orientation of their enterprises to the market rather than to home consumption. Though agronomic response to fertilizer is generally favorable, the response is not always economically attractive. In some countries, owing to excessively high fertilizer prices, agronomic response must be extremely favorable to pay for the increases obtained. In some lands attempts are being made to influence the pattern of farm production by control of the distribution of fertilizers or of farmer credit for fertilizer. In the Philippines a fertilizer subsidy has favored paddy lands over sugar cane since 1956.

Since World War II, the U.S. programs for foreign assistance, private foundations, and other agencies both public and private have carried on a highly advanced science and technology program in plant improvement, using selection and breeding techniques common in Europe and North America. Many varieties originating in the highly developed countries were immediately successful in other parts of the world, yielding much better than their indigenous counterparts. The introduction of methods of plant breeding and selection to find germ plasm better suited to local conditions became a prominent part of the aid programs of the advanced countries for their rapidly emerging neighbors. An outstanding contribution of this kind to the welfare of a great land area was made by the vigorous crop improvement program introduced in Latin America by The Rockefeller Foundation in cooperation with existing indigenous research agencies. The results of these efforts have been spectacular. In Chile, for example, The Rockefeller Foundation in cooperation with the Chilean Ministry of Agriculture was investigating 4000 lines of wheat in 1961.

A bean improvement program beginning at the Rural University of the State of Minas Gerais, Brazil, with the cooperation of Purdue University, has resulted in an average yield of 1163 kg/ha from many trials with better varieties, as compared with a general farmer average for the area of 700 kg/ha (Vieira, 1962). Brazil produces about one-fifth of the world's beans (FAO, 1961, p. 84). Variety trials with corn in the same region produced yields of 81 bushels per acre in contrast to an average of 20 bushels for all Brazil (Instituto Agronômico, 1960). Purdue is also cooperating under AID auspices with the Rural University of Minas Gerais in a soybean improvement program. Research workers on this project are stimulated by the apparent adaptability of soybeans to the Minas Gerais area and by the realization of the great need for more protein in the diets of animals and people in Brazil. Soy varieties in plots at Viçosa in 1958–1959 yielded 2751 kg/ha, about 41 bushels per acre (Brandão, 1961). In the same year the average production in Brazil was 1330 kg/ha, in Italy 1889 kg/ha, and in the United States 1629 kg/ha (FAO, 1961, p. 116). In that year soybeans were grown on about 10,000,000 hectares in the United States and on only 114,000 hectares in Brazil. In the Cauca Valley, Colombia, improved corn varieties with supporting cultural practices have produced 7000 kg/ha as compared with 2000 kg/ha with the old varieties, according to a director of an experiment station in the valley.

Other technological practices being adapted and adopted by the emerging nations include those of land reclamation, such as leveling, terracing, gully filling, drainage, and irrigation; and those of soil conservation, such as terracing, building of dams, establishing waterways, the use of trees and grass on slopes, contouring, "minimum tillage," and others. Newer methods of pest and weed control which depend heavily on new chemicals are being introduced. Even with herbicides, weed control is still quite dependent on improved methods of mechanical cultivation.

The research necessary to develop the better varieties and to adapt fertilizer practices and other techniques of modern agriculture to untried areas fits naturally into the capacities and the facilities of the developing nations. However, adequate technical and scientific leadership and guidance must be made available to train the indigenous research workers in the necessary research technology, organization, and management. This has been well started in many places. It is not at all uncommon to find in the developing nations, especially of Latin America, many large field experiment stations, well managed and committed to intensive plot experimentation. The still abundant supply of cheap labor in these countries simplifies the problem of meeting the great labor load of such experimentation. There are several field experiment stations in Latin American countries which in size of land area involved, numbers of experiments, and numbers of individual plots equal or surpass many of the experimental farms of our land-grant universities.

Lack of Adequate Education and Research on Crop Production

In most, if not all, of the newly developing countries agricultural education and research are lagging. Often the lag is greater than can be justified by the level of economy and the general stage of development of the nation involved. This results from long-entrenched mores and cultural backgrounds with their influence on attitudes toward social responsibility, education, research, and technology. The cultural attitudes inherited from the Old World by the New seem to have followed closely lines of latitude. The early development of freedom of the university from the state in northern Europe and England was transmitted to North America, where public attitudes toward the state-supported schools early permitted operation free from outside political influence. Furthermore, in the United States the concept of a broad base of public education was applied at the university level by the Land-Grant Act. At the time of the passage of that important act, the leadership in this country still carried a heavy representation from a pioneer society where hard work and the application of knowledge to everyday life was considered sensible and proper.

The orientation of good scientific effort toward the solution of practical problems by the land-grant colleges and experiment stations and the United States Department of Agriculture brought an extremely rapid solution of the problems of agriculture. The success of this approach was possible largely because the research workers in these institutions came largely from agrarian backgrounds, only a generation or two removed from the frontier, where hard manual labor was sociably acceptable. Bright, well trained, and practical, to them it seemed quite logical to apply science to practical problems. The phenomenon of a rigorous, well trained scientist who also was a scholar and a gentleman, intensely eager to use his skills in the solution of the real problems around him and willing to work alongside less educated workers in a sweaty, dusty, muddy operation, was something new in the world.

Simultaneously with the development of this approach toward agricultural research, an educational movement appeared, principally in the land-grant colleges, which was aimed at training people in the skills of husbandry and mechanical arts. First largely aimed at training only in skills, this type of education soon grew into a highly sophisticated pattern of training involving the most rigorous sciences and their application to solving real problems. This approach to research and education is generally lacking in the developing nations. It is not well understood by many scientists and educators even in our country. They frequently do not have an adequate concept of the depth of the training now required in agricultural curricula, the dynamics of its challenge, and the stimulation it offers to students.

In the developing countries such concepts of research and education have in general been lacking. Cultural patterns have been those in which trained men disdain to work with their hands. There has been little understanding of the coordination needed to ensure the easy flow of the most basic research findings into various stages of developmental research and testing and eventually into the solution of practical problems. There has been little appreciation of the smoothly functioning mechanics of a university extension system which takes research results to the people.

Cultural traditions may seriously hinder progress within the university in many ways. The election of professors to positions of eminence—"the chair"—and the election of university administrators by faculty and even students, although democratic, is clearly not in the interest of capable or competent administration. Most faculties soon shake down to a few competing political camps. Thus political trading tends to replace competence as the basis for recognition. Successful candidates find their freedom of action and judgment restricted by previous commitments.

Educational institutions and experiment stations are usually separate organizations with little cooperation between the two. The extension programs introduced in several countries are also too frequently carried as separate programs, not embodied in a unified effort of research and education. Consequently the extension personnel lose the stimulus of contact with a large body of scientific fellows and must expend much energy in locating sources of new information. Also, research and teaching programs suffer from lack of contact with professional colleagues working daily with real agricultural problems.

The exportation of new technologies from the developed countries to their emerging neighbors has not been as difficult as the exportation of the philosophy which has resulted in a highly effective application of science to the betterment of people. This is recognized by many leaders in agricultural research and education in the developing lands, especially those who have had opportunity to observe cultural patterns and attitudes in other parts of the world. The senior author visited with a dean of a prominent agricultural college in Colombia who lamented the fact that there were only 900 *agrónomos* in his country, where 2000 were needed. He was disturbed that farm boys were not coming to the university. He said that generally the only farm boys to matriculate were those from the rich, landed families. Apparently educational opportunity for the sons of the average farmers, who were poor, was quite meager.

A major stumbling block to agricultural progress in many emerging nations is the dearth of comprehensive problem-oriented research programs conducted within the agricultural universities. Such programs are necessary to complement other university services in order that agronomic science may contribute fully to the scientific and technological growth of the nation. Teaching methods frequently do not allow excellence in undergraduate teaching. Too often, because textbooks are not available in the native languages, students must rely on notes from lectures. Expositional presentation of facts to be learned, with little encouragement to critical analysis and debate, is too common a teaching technique. In Latin American countries at least, the undergraduate is often equally trained in nearly every phase of agriculture from agricultural engineering through agronomy and animal science to food technology and rural economics. This system, combined with insufficient training in critical analysis, tends to produce a generalist inadequately prepared to direct critical thought to the solving of the problems which will confront him.

The teaching "machinery" used is usually not geared to turning out sufficient numbers of competent agronomic scientists. In the *catedrático* (chair) system, training above the undergraduate level is on an individual basis. The trainee works closely with an established professor over a relatively long period of time in a program of individual instruction and practice. Since there is a tendency to limit the number of "chairs," only small numbers of scientists can be trained in this manner. Although they do receive close personal attention, they miss the broadening influence of contact with several professionals.

In developing nations, higher education is frequently unbalanced, offering many courses in the humanities and law but few in science and engineering. The universities are usually poorly equipped with libraries and laboratories and rely heavily on ill trained, part-time teachers. This is the direct result of inadequate financing. It costs from one-fourth to one-sixth as much to provide law courses as courses in engineering and science. This has been particularly the case in Colombia, where in 1962 there were only 1150 students in technical institutes as compared with 23,000 in universities (Harbison, 1963, p. 143). Colombia, which is sometimes classified as a "partly developed" country along with some other countries of Latin America and nations such as Turkey, Iran, Pakistan, and Ghana, has 25 universities with 1.8 per cent of its college-age population enrolled.

Outlining the main characteristics and problems of higher education in Latin America, Olcese (1963), in an address at the recent "Agronomy in the Americas" program of the American Society of Agronomy, listed the following: (1) There is a lack of professors on a full-time basis; (2) the training of these professors is deficient; (3) professors do very little research or none at all; (4) teaching is done in a very theoretical way; (5) the curriculum offered is very rigid; (6) no specialization is offered; (7) use of facilities or areas within the university is not made fully available; (8) professors are not appointed to a department; (9) salaries of professors are very low; (10) physical facilities are poor; (11) programs of the courses are very weak; (12) administrative structure is inadequate; (13) little attention is given to the students.

SUMMARY

Plant agriculture in the emerging nations is advancing rapidly, but is barely staying ahead of increasing population. Average world production and population figures are, however, somewhat misleading owing to gross inequality in distribution of food and population. For 1962–1963, the Food and Agriculture Organization reports an appreciable per caput food production increase for Africa and the Near East, a loss for Latin America, and a slight increase for the Far East.

A relatively short time is required to increase productivity by bringing new technology to bear in developing areas, as shown by wheat and rice yield increases from various parts of the world.

In many emerging nations, a one-crop agriculture has been practiced and has proved to be very unstable financially, politically, and agronomically. Brazilian sugar and coffee are examples.

New technology, such as the use of commercial fertilizers and improved varieties, is being applied, sometimes incompletely and not uniformly, but with some outstanding successes in production increases. Fertilizer used on Brazilian pastures raised beef production from 301 to 703 kilograms per hectare; increased wheat yields in Chile to 90 bushels per acre; and in Colombia not only increased wheat yields to 115 bushels per acre but produced 80 metric tons of potatoes on the same land the same year. New varieties of beans and soybeans in Brazil are shown to be capable of doubling present yields. Similar increases are possible for corn and other crops.

Although known technology is shown to be capable of impressive production increases, the point is made that a changed philosophy concerning agricultural research and educational institutions is necessary for a permanent solution of the production problems in the emerging nations.

Support is given to the establishment of problem-oriented university research programs, graduate-level agricultural education, and agricultural university extension in the emerging nations.

REFERENCES

BRANDÃO, S. S. 1961. Contribuicão ao estudo de variedades de soja. *Experientiae, 1*, No. 4 (Aug.). Publication of the Research Service of the Rural University of the State of Minas Gerais, Viçosa, M. G., Brazil.

DAVIS, KINGSLEY. 1963. Population. *Sci. American, 209*, No. 3, 62–71.

FAO. 1961. *Production Yearbook, 1961*. Vol. 15. Food and Agriculture Organization of the United Nations, Rome.

FAO. 1963. *The State of Food and Agriculture, 1963*. Food and Agriculture Organization of the United Nations, Rome.

FURTADO, CELSO. 1963. The development of Brazil. *Sci. American, 209*, No. 3, 208–223.

HARBISON, FREDERICK. 1963. Education for development. *Sci. American, 209*, No. 3, 140–147.

Instituto Agronômico, Belo Horizonte, Minas Gerais, Brazil. 1960. Mimeographed data.

OLCESE, ORLANDO. 1963. Present status, problems, and future prospects of agricultural education in Latin America. Presented at American Society of Agronomy Special Program, "Agronomy in the Americas," Denver, Colo.

QUINN, L. R., G. O. MOTT, and W. V. A. BISCHOFF. 1961. *Fertilization of Colonial Guinea Grass Pastures and Beef Production with Zebu Steers*. International Basic Economy Corporation, Research Institute Bull. 24.

SCRIMSHAW, NEVIN S. 1963. Food. *Sci. American, 209*, No. 3, 72–91.

VIEIRA, CLIBAS. 1962. Contribuicão ao melhoramento do feijoeiro (*Phaseolus vulgaris* L.) no Estado de Minas Gerais. Unpublished thesis, Escola Superior de Agricultura, Viçosa, Minas Gerais, Brazil.

Research to Devise and Adapt

Innovations

Research to Improve Production of Corn in Asia

ERNEST W. SPRAGUE

Geneticist, The Rockefeller Foundation, New Delhi, India

THE YIELDS OF CEREALS in Southeast Asia are extremely low; national averages in these countries are very similar and none have changed significantly for many years. This indicates that soils, climate, and cereals have reached an equilibrium as expressed in production potential. Unless man exerts a concentrated effort to improve both varieties and cultural practices, there will be little change in the future.

To improve varieties and change cultural practices, a multitude of factors must be dealt with simultaneously. Man's preferences as to the types of cereals which compose his diet as well as deep-seated traditions conditioned by habit and religion are things that must be understood and taken into account. Other factors that the researcher must consider in approaching the problem of cereal improvement are: available funds, manpower, research facilities, and availability of suitable germ plasm.

The discussion in this paper will be built around corn, drawing from the writer's experience primarily in India and, to a lesser extent, in Thailand, Indonesia, and Vietnam.

Corn is a relatively young crop in this part of the world and has not, until recently, been considered important. It is now recognized throughout Southeast Asia as a very important crop, and considerable research effort is being directed to its improvement. The need for corn improvement work can best be illustrated by the fact that in 1962 over 11 million acres were grown in India at an average yield of only 15.7 bushels per acre. For the same year, Thailand's corn yield on 830,000 acres was 32.3 bushels per acre; that of the Philippines, 9.4 bushels per acre on nearly 5 million acres; and Indonesia's yield was 16.4 bushels per acre on 7.75 million acres. In 1962, the United States produced 64.1 bushels per acre on nearly 57 million acres. For the period 1955 to 1959 the average yield was 59.8 bushels per acre for the United States and 12.9, 21.7, 9.8, and 14.8 bushels per acre for India, Thailand, the Philippines, and Indonesia, respectively. In these four countries 5 million more acres were grown in 1962 than the average for the period 1955 to 1959.[1]

Although both acreage and yields have been slightly increased in this recent period owing to improvement programs, the corn yields in Southeast Asia are only 15 to 50 per cent of the United States average yield. The relatively high yields in Thailand are due to a shifting to new land, and to an increase in acreage caused by new land's being brought into cultivation. Land in Thailand that has been in production for many years is producing low crop yields more in line with those in the other Asian countries. An average yield in Asia equal to or above that recorded in the United States is a very realistic possibility; this will be discussed later. There is also a great potential for increasing acreage planted to corn throughout Southeast Asia.

DEVELOPMENT OF THE CORN IMPROVEMENT PROGRAM IN INDIA

The first corn improvement program in India was initiated in 1945. By 1956, there were three or four improvement programs, all independent of one another. Although much diligent effort went into these programs, they did not make a significant contribution to improved corn production in their early years.

No doubt several factors influenced the amount of progress made, but the most important single factor was lack of suitable germ plasm. Corn has been grown in India for about four hundred years, but there is strong evidence to indicate that they have only two types within the country. Unfortunately, both these types are from very narrow germ plasm backgrounds. The corn breeders had very little opportunity to develop better-performing varieties or hybrids from these sources.

With the local germ plasm, agronomists were unable to demon-

---

[1] U. S. Department of Agriculture, Foreign Agricultural Service, *World Agricultural Production and Trade*, Statistical Report, Nov. 1963.

Indian villagers greeting the Union and Gujarat state Ministers of Agriculture and the chairman of the board of the National Seeds Corporation.

A broad base of germ plasm is available for use in international varietal improvement programs. *Above,* lines introduced from the Western Hemisphere. *Below,* lines native to India; small ears at left, primitive types from Sikkim.

Locally made items of equipment are completely satisfactory for the researchers' needs.

Chapathis made of sorghum, maize, and wheat form an important part of the diet in northern India.

strate the value of high fertility in corn production because they were dealing with varieties that were not capable of high yield even under the best agronomic practices. Agronomists logically concluded that 40 pounds of nitrogen per acre was about the maximum fertility level that should be recommended for corn. Low-fertility practices coupled with inadequate weed and water control were strong retarding influences on the progress of Indian corn improvement.

A few of the Indian leaders and foreign technical advisers, however, realized the potential of corn in Asia and were looking for a way to give the crop the emphasis that they believed it should have. In 1954, the Government of India invited Drs. Wellhausen and Grant of The Rockefeller Foundation to survey India to determine the potential for corn and to put forth ideas for a research program in corn improvement. They recommended the introduction of a wider range of germ plasm and the setting up of a coordinated program on a national scale. As a result of this recommendation, new germ plasm was immediately sent into India.

In 1957, a new coordinated corn-breeding program on a national scale was initiated by the Indian Council of Agricultural Research in cooperation with the various state governments and The Rockefeller Foundation. Later, two agricultural universities were included in the program.

This program was designed to have four major corn-breeding centers to handle the major breeding work, and nine regional subcenters that initially would function as regional testing stations. The four major centers represent four agro-climatic zones in which corn is an important crop. The nine subcenters are distributed to represent more specific areas within the agro-climatic zones. These stations are financed by the Indian Council of Agricultural Research but administered by the state department of agriculture or university where they are located. The Indian Agricultural Research Institute, which is a Central Government research and educational institute at New Delhi, was selected as one of the four major stations. This station accepted the responsibility for being the coordinating center.

The Indian Council of Agricultural Research, which is an advisory and financing body of the Central Government's Ministry of

Agriculture, provides the budget for staff and operation at each station. These funds are incorporated into the state government or university budget and are administered by the state government or university. The recipient state government or university also supplies the physical facilities. In this way the state departments of agriculture or universities, as the case may be, feel that they are a genuine part of the national program. Within this arrangement, a true spirit of cooperation has developed.

The Rockefeller Foundation, cooperating in this program, contributes services of a limited number of technical personnel and furnishes supplies and equipment that are not available within the country but are essential for the operation of a large research program. This includes tractors, transportation, spare parts, and special research equipment.

The program for varietal improvement was laid out and in order for operation in early 1957. The problem then confronting the coordinating office was how to initiate this ambitious program and develop true cooperation at the individual level. In this connection it must be remembered that very few of the local personnel had any previous experience with corn, and also that their pattern of operation in the past had been one of independent endeavor rather than a cooperative approach.

Many immediate problems existed, such as what germ plasm to concentrate on; how to distribute the work load; how to manage problems related to cultural practices; what fertility levels should be used in the breeding program; and what diseases and insects were most important.

Small plantings were made in 1957 at several locations. This first planting consisted primarily of germ plasm sources from various parts of the world, to identify the materials that should receive attention. Experiences during the first year very vividly pointed out an urgent need for training in corn breeding for the staff and, above all, the need for developing and improving the experimental fields.

Early 1958 saw the start of a concentrated effort to develop the experimental fields. In the initial stages, The Rockefeller Foundation provided an experiment station operations man on two different occasions for short assignments to advise and to accelerate the development. Following the pattern of The Rockefeller Foundation's philosophy, their cooperating staff worked side by side with the Indian staff in an effort to impart as much on-the-job training as possible in the development of experimental fields, and to demonstrate the value of having well developed fields. "Development" in this discussion refers to land leveling, drainage, irrigation, and all-around good farming practices. This type of training is extremely important throughout Southeast Asia, since many of the agricultural scientists in this area do not have agricultural backgrounds, nor have they been exposed to actual practice of agriculture during their education.

Although experiment station development has received a great deal of attention since 1958, it is still one of the weakest areas of the corn improvement program, both in terms of implementation and in terms of understanding on the part of the staff. It should be pointed out here that the majority of the staff in India, Thailand, and Indonesia understand the importance of well managed fields, but there is little understanding of how well managed fields are either attained or maintained.

Mr. A. D. Pandit, vice president of the Indian Council of Agricultural Research, stressed the importance of well managed research stations when he said, "Unless we can show that substantial increases in agricultural production over the present average level in the country are being brought about year by year in our experimental farms with methods which are within the reach of the ordinary farmer and which will give him a substantially higher net return from the farm than at present, we cannot hope to build up the faith of the farmer in our research institutions or our extension workers." [2]

Although rather broad objectives were laid down at the time when this program was developed, the coordinating office technically responsible for developing and implementing the program felt that, initially, rather narrow, well defined objectives should be emphasized. Basically, these objectives were on-the-job training of staff, and development of desirable hybrids in the shortest possible time.

With the approval of the Indian Council of Agricultural Re-

[2] A. D. Pandit, "Orient research to farmer's problems," *Indian Farming*, 13, No. 5, 19–20, 1963.

search and the Indian Agricultural Research Institute, a six-month training period was set up, during which candidates from the various stations participated in the program at the Research Center in New Delhi under the direction of the coordinators and the Delhi staff. This made it possible for technicians to go through one entire cycle of the breeding program in the field. An effort was made to involve the candidates in every phase of the program, so that they would have a better understanding not only of corn breeding per se, but also of keeping and handling the records, storing and cataloguing seed, and analyzing and interpreting data. This pattern proved to be very effective in the early years. In every session there would be one or two exceptionally good technicians who, after their training period, went back to their respective stations and really upgraded the local program.

The coordinators believed that if they were going to be effective they must know the genetic material and its responses intimately at each station. They also felt that they must know each staff member, both technical and nontechnical, and learn to understand their problems and their strong and weak points, in order to be able to develop functional cooperation. They also had to know the administrative people concerned, in order to take problems to them in an objective manner. To accomplish this, the coordinators traveled from station to station at appropriate times and studied the material in the fields with the station staff. More often than not, the coordinators helped with the planting, irrigation, pollination work, and other jobs at hand when they visited the stations. They also tried to be available on call to help any station with its problems. This method of coordination and participation served as an effective teaching practice and as a strong cement to bind the entire group of corn improvement people together.

As an additional medium for training and communication, an annual progress report was put together which included all the work done at all the stations. This report is distributed to all the stations and to the administrative offices concerned with each station. Following the distribution of the progress report, the technicians and some of the administrative people attend an annual conference to discuss materials, progress, and problems of the over-all program.

Although the agronomists had data showing that Indian corn

would not respond profitably to nitrogen applications above 40 pounds per acre, it was thought that the breeding program should be based on a somewhat higher fertility level. Therefore, at the outset, the breeding program operated on a fertilizer application of 80 pounds of nitrogen and about 60 pounds of P_2O_5 per acre. This seemingly high level received considerable criticism, but the corn breeders held fast to their idea that they must have sufficient fertility to allow superior germ plasm to express itself. It is interesting to note that at present the corn breeders are using, without opposition, 135 pounds of nitrogen per acre balanced with P_2O_5 and K_2O. This history of the use of fertilizer in the breeding program is important and interesting, as the same general pattern has also developed in Thailand and Indonesia. That is, as better germ plasm and cultural practices are used, responses to higher levels of fertility are obtained.

From the initial screening, it became apparent that the germ plasm from South America should receive a great deal of attention. Sources from other areas were also very promising. On the basis of this information, many inbred lines from Colombia and from the southern United States were put into the program. There were also many inbred lines from India that had been developed before the coordinated program. Inbred lines were tested very extensively in top-cross tests while new lines were simultaneously being developed from a variety of materials.

Within a relatively short time, large collections of inbred lines had been narrowed down to what were called "cream" lines. These cream lines had performed consistently well at several testing locations. As early as possible, 52 lines, covering a wide range of germ plasm, were identified as potential parents and put into tests to determine the best possible combinations. From this test 10 lines from four diverse germ plasm sources were ultimately selected to form the parentage of four hybrids.

SEED PRODUCTION DEVELOPMENT

At this stage two problems faced the research people. One was the matter of getting improved varieties to the farmers in the shortest possible time, and the other was the lack of an improved seed program to provide seed. The easy way out would have been to put production in the hands of the breeders. This, of course, in the long run would not have been practical, as it would have greatly retarded research. The breeders did agree, however, to help build seed supplies as quickly as possible and help a production program phase into an organization to handle seed.

In November 1960, the breeders had sufficient data to predict the parentage of the four hybrids, although they had not actually seen the hybrids. On the basis of the predicted performance and the understanding that a seed organization would be developed, the breeders, during the winter of 1960–1961, increased the ten inbred lines and made up single crosses and double crosses. At the 1961 conference, which was held in February, the four hybrids were released. By spring of 1961, the framework and a limited number of people were available to handle the foundation seed production, and a few acres of double-cross production were put out with farmer producers.

To test these hybrids during 1961, the breeders developed an extensive regional testing program which extended far beyond the cooperating research stations. It was thought that this must be done because the hybrids were released and in production and the breeders, as yet, had not had an opportunity to see them. Also, it was believed that this would be a very good extension tool. At this time, although the corn improvement people were convinced of the superiority of this material and the advantages of adequate levels of fertility, the extension and community development people had not been close enough to the research to understand the advances that had taken place in four years. The regional testing served as a means of bringing the extension and community development people into closer contact with progress made at the research level.

The Rockefeller Foundation cooperated with the Indian Council of Agricultural Research in developing the National Seeds Corporation as a private limited company whose main function is to promote the production and distribution of quality seeds throughout the country. This corporation was set up to deal first with corn seed, but it is expected to develop, with time and the release of new varieties of other crops, into an organization dealing with foundation seed of many crops.

During the beginning years of operation, the seed organization handled all the foundation seed, and it attempted to handle certified seed through contract growing with farmers. This arrangement, of course, left the organization with the job of distribution. Many people felt very strongly that the function of the National Seeds Corporation should be restricted to the production of foundation seed and the promotion of good seed. There were other factions, however, that believed that all seed production should be kept under the direction and supervision of the seed organization and that all sales of certified seed should be handled by it. Admittedly, in the initial stages it was necessary for the seed organization to take the lead in order to allow private seed growers an opportunity to phase into the program.

Through patience and firm pressure several of the more progressive seed growers were able to develop effective seed production and sales operations. As the seed growers became stronger, the seed organization began to relax on some of its ideas, which made it easier for seed growers to develop the concept of seed-producing companies.

At the present time there are private growers, cooperatives, and seed companies that are operating with a relatively free hand. Within this group of certified seed producers, the largest one is involved with a United States company. The National Seeds Corporation provides the foundation seed, field inspection, and seed certification services to all the seed growers. It also reserves the right to refuse foundation seed to a grower who does not comply with the seed standards or misrepresents his product. In other words, the National Seeds Corporation now functions as a foundation seed–producing organization, a regulatory organization, and a promoter of good seed. These were the functions that were in mind as far back as 1960 when the framework of the organization was first drawn up.

The United States Agency for International Development (AID) Mission to India helped financially and technically to organize and develop the National Seeds Corporation and lent technical support in the initial stages. The agronomists of the AID Mission were particularly interested in extending the use of hybrid seed and fertilizer, and they concentrated most of their effort on developing demonstration techniques with the local extension agencies. They worked toward the organization of a relatively small but well conducted demonstration program, with the thought that demonstrations should not be put out unless they were properly conducted. Mr. A. D. Pandit expressed very similar views when he said, "Demonstrations should be organized only by competent and qualified agricultural graduates and they should not be allotted to VLWs [village level workers] who have had, in some cases, less than a year's acquaintance with the theory and practice of agricultural sciences."[3]

DEVELOPMENT OF INTERDISCIPLINE RESEARCH

The corn program started in 1957 was known as the Coordinated Maize Breeding Scheme. As indicated by the title of the project and organization, the staff were plant breeders and emphasis was to be placed on developing suitable hybrids. The breeders were engaged in continually studying varieties and building new germ plasm complexes.

It became apparent that unless investigations were started on soil fertility, disease, and insect problems, the full potential of corn would never be realized. With the breeding program reasonably well organized, the breeders asked the Indian Council of Agricultural Research to organize programs in the other major disciplines. The Council's budgets are organized on a five-year basis which fits into India's five-year plans, therefore extra money could not be made available. The Council did, however, give the coordinators permission to do what they considered most important within the allotted budget. Plans were drawn up for fertility and plant population investigations and were presented at the 1961 conference. These plans were accepted by the breeders, and agronomic investigations were started in 1961.

Plans were drawn up for a corn improvement program coordinating not only the breeding work, but also research in agronomy, pathology, and entomology. These plans were accepted in principle, and the budget set up for the Third Five-Year Plan (1961) included the corn improvement program with provision for staff and research in the four major disciplines. This has made the corn pro-

[3] A. D. Pandit, *op. cit.*, p. 52.

gram much more effective and promises to be a very good example of the importance of cooperation and coordination within and among disciplines.

A similar example comes from Thailand. In 1960, the Government of Thailand and the United States AID Mission to Thailand expressed interest in the Indian corn improvement program and its organization, and sent Dr. Breitenbach of the Mission and Mr. Ampol of the Department of Agriculture to India to study the program. On the basis of their visit and several visits to Thailand by the coordinator of the Indian program, a coordinated corn improvement program was organized in Thailand. Before 1960, the Department of Agriculture and the Agricultural University had independent corn improvement programs. Within each of these the four disciplines were operating independently of one another. In essence, there were eight different units working on corn. These were put together in a coordinated program. The Thais are very proud of their program, which is making rapid progress in corn improvement.

The breeders in all the Southeast Asian countries are much interested in obtaining better germ plasm. Fortunately, much of the germ plasm of Mexico, Central America, and South America can be used to their advantage. In the Indian corn program, there are very promising inbred lines in trial that represent germ plasm from India, Colombia, Peru, Mexico, Venezuela, the Caribbean area, Kenya, and the United States.

New complexes are now available in all the countries referred to in this paper that have yield potentials superior to those of the varieties or hybrids previously released. With simple breeding procedures there is every reason to believe that even higher-yielding varieties can be developed from these complexes in a short time. It has been shown by many investigators that improved open-pollinated varieties can be developed quickly from high-yielding complexes. These methods are simpler than developing hybrids, and eliminate the costly and difficult task of hybrid seed production and distribution. Understanding these methods and their advantages, corn breeders in Thailand and Indonesia are directing their programs toward varietal improvement. More and more attention is being given to varietal improvement in India and the

Philippines, and it is quite possible that these programs will, in the future, release improved open-pollinated varieties as well as hybrids.

The recommended hybrids for each agro-climatic zone of India are being tested at eight locations under different levels of fertility. Yields up to 140 bushels per acre have been observed. The highest average yield for a given fertilizer level has been 98 bushels per acre, and the average yield of the most economical treatment for all the eight stations is 90 bushels per acre. Yields of 160 bushels per acre have been recorded from experimental material not yet released which may raise the economic production potential still further. Indonesia, in 1963, reported a yield of 104 bushels per acre from a cross between an Indian variety and a variety from Colombia; this was 32 bushels per acre more than their recommended variety.[4]

Yields of 90 to 140 bushels per acre are not high as compared with the best yields in the United States, but yields of this magnitude after only a relatively short period of intensified research indicate a high potential for corn in Southeast Asia.

Developing a Research Program

In developing agricultural research programs in countries where funds, training, and background are somewhat limited, it is important that objectives and methods be established that will best fit the needs. The most suitable methods and materials may often be quite different from those best understood and practiced by scientists from the United States.

The most expedient method is the importation of improved varieties and/or practices from other parts of the world. Caution must be exercised in such an importation program. Varieties from other areas may yield well, but may have inherent problems caused by diseases and insects to which they carry no resistance. In many cases the grain type of imported varieties is not suited to the people. A typical example is corn in India. Many open-pedigree hybrids from the United States yield very well in India and at one

---

[4] Figures from unpublished data.

time received considerable attention. The dent grain, however, is completely unacceptable to the Indian people. Moreover, when production of some of these hybrids was attempted, it was found that the parental inbred lines were not adapted to India and were virtually impossible to produce there. This then would require the importation of single crosses from the United States for the production of double-cross or certified seed. Foreign exchange automatically makes such a procedure impracticable.

Facilities supplied by cooperators in international development programs should be selected on the basis of the recipient's needs. This applies even to simple tools. In many cases highly developed research tools are not as reliable under adverse conditions as more rugged but simpler implements. Moisture testers and calculators commonly used in the United States are not as reliable or convenient as hand-operated units. In determining what types of equipment to buy, a great deal of attention should be given to the conditions under which equipment is to be used and the probable skills of the operators. It is shocking to see thousands of dollars' worth of equipment in the Asian countries which is not in operation mainly because it is too complicated, or is not suited to the conditions of the area.

In making up equipment lists for cereal research it is advisable to discuss at length with the host technicians the objectives of the project, the skill of the people working on the project, the availability and reliability of electricity, and the availability and reliability of instrument repair shops. A problem in this context is that of funds for repair. Often a piece of equipment is out of order for want of a relatively small repair because the technician is unable to get funds or because the item needed is not available in his country. A small breakdown can render an expensive machine valueless to the project. Much of the difficulty could be eliminated if more appropriate research tools were provided, and, equally important, if the donor provided funds for repairs and importation of parts. At the very least, such provisions should be guaranteed by the host or recipient at the time equipment lists are approved.

In setting up methods or procedures for research, it must be borne in mind that only a limited number of trained people will be available to carry out the research. Another important consideration is that the production levels to be raised are usually so low that substantial improvement can be made by very simple methods. One can see by visual observation the difference between 15 and 50 bushels per acre. With these thoughts in mind, it becomes rather obvious that in initiating a program very simple but effective methods should be employed. This approach is cheaper, just as effective, and faster. Equally important, it allows training of the staff so that more adequate techniques can be used when the objective becomes a smaller increase in production, say from 100 up to 125 bushels per acre. If the complicated methods necessary for determining small gains are adopted early in the program, the inefficiency and errors due to lack of training will more than offset the advantages that these methods may have over the more simplified approach.

Uniformity and coordination are very important and time-saving factors in any research program. These are also the factors most difficult to attain. Many people feel that some of their prerogatives are being denied when they are asked to conform to a uniform system and cooperate in an over-all program. Uniformity increases efficiency in teaching by requiring only one system of records, data, and seed cataloguing, and also in developing field books, seed registers, and analyses of data. Coordination increases efficiency by bringing about a free interchange of information and material, and is often an effective guarantee that participating technicians will not deviate from the established objectives.

Continuity of financial and technical support over an extended period is so important that without it very little can be accomplished. Local nationals should develop and eventually take over any program, and local governments should eventually take over financial responsibilities. It takes a long time, however, to develop staffing patterns and train personnel that are adequate for the full responsibility of an important research program. It also takes a long time to demonstrate to the local government the need of strong financial support and the necessity of local nationals' being assigned and promoted in these jobs. The usual tendency is for people to be shifted to new jobs for promotion or to be given additional responsibilities. Either of these common practices retards progress.

The host country requires time to organize and fully support the agricultural research that is so vital to it. Until the time when local nationals and local funds can be worked into the program and take it over, the continuity of foreign technical help is extremely important. The foreign technician should be able to spend the number of years necessary on the project without interruption. All too often a good man is rotated out after a relatively short time and a new man rotated in with the same or similar responsibilities. Also, in many cases, complete technical support is removed too soon. When these things occur the local technicians' efficiency is greatly retarded. With well defined objectives, there is no substitute for continuity of a good foreign technician's participation in the project.

Very often projects with well defined objectives of increased food production based on one or two key food crops of national importance can be used to demonstrate ways and means whereby a host country can become self-sufficient in agricultural research and administration. The systems producing progress in this way will filter into other areas of research, so that the cooperators' efforts soon spread far beyond the area that they are actively engaged in. Very broad objectives, on the other hand, are often not supported financially or technically to the degree necessary for satisfactory progress.

SUMMARY

In developing a research program with a host country, be sure there are well defined objectives that meet the mutual interests of the cooperator and the host and cover the needs of the host country. Guest technicians working with the nationals of a country usually work best if arrangements are made whereby they are part of and participate in the endeavors rather than functioning as advisers. It is then up to the guest technician to develop the friendships and relationships with the nationals that will gain him their respect and make his leadership effective.

It is necessary to provide flexibility in budgets that fill needs which local budgets do not meet. Projects should be adequately supported, but overfinancing should be avoided. One great problem in the Southeast Asian area is lack of flexibility in research budgets and costly delays through administrative procedures.

It is also necessary to develop training to qualify people for responsible positions, and build into programs possibilities for trained people to have stability of base of operation and continuity of objectives. Within the coordination, a multiple-discipline approach should be developed that is effective and acceptable to the administration.

Guest technicians should build nationals into responsible areas of the program by making it possible for them to carry more and more responsibility, yet should be available for backstopping. This can be done by working closely in a cooperative spirit which allows the nationals' ideas to be expressed and used.

Animal and Veterinary Science Programs in Developing Countries

FREDERICK N. ANDREWS

Vice President for Research and Dean of the Graduate School, Purdue University, Lafayette, Indiana

IT IS IN MANY WAYS unfortunate that we in the United States have so often referred to the undeveloped, the underdeveloped, and the emerging nations. As a result, many abroad, and all too many at home, have concluded that we have a system that needs little improvement and, indeed, should be copied, as is, throughout the world. In discussing my assigned topic I plan to describe programs and problems in the animal sciences which involve food production as such, certain relationships of animal and human health, and the kind of training needed for the development of effective programs in the animal sciences.

Let us first demolish the myth that we North Americans have a mature and stable program that cannot be improved upon. During the 25,000 years or less since the domestication of animals, there has been less than half a century of radical change. During the past quarter of a century we have seen the United States change from dependence upon animal fats to extensive use of those of vegetable origin. Urbanization and the steady change in work habits have made us a nation seeking to avoid calories rather than one hungry for them. There has been a steady decrease in the per capita consumption of fluid milk, and a remarkable increase in the per capita consumption of poultry meat. Our numbers of dairy cows have steadily declined, but milk production per cow has more than doubled. The breeds of chickens developed by several generations of family-type poultry breeders have virtually disappeared, and a few strains or lines of scientifically developed meat- and egg-type chickens dominate the U.S. market and, in fact, most of the world. The establishment of the soybean in the Midwest revolutionized animal-feeding methods, and the development of new corn and sorghum varieties had the practical effect of making most of the United States a part of the corn belt. The control and virtual elimination of tuberculosis and brucellosis in animals has had a profound effect on human health, but our own livestock industry must constantly be on guard against outbreaks of hog cholera, respiratory diseases which affect poultry, cattle, and swine, and a great variety of parasites; and we have imposed many restrictions on the importation of animals and animal products because of the vulnerability of our livestock to foot-and-mouth disease.

Although we have just celebrated the centennial of the land-grant colleges, it would be misleading to imply that we have an educational system that has ripened into a mature and perfect fruit. There is no doubt in my own mind that the land-grant university has played a unique role in the agricultural, economic, and social development of the United States, but there is likewise no doubt in my mind that the land-grant universities are in the midst of dynamic changes which will be greater in the next quarter of a century than during all of the first hundred years.

It is with this background, recognizing that we are still evolving our own patterns of animal food production and of education in the sciences related to agriculture, that I will describe some of the animal and veterinary science problems and programs of *other* developing nations.

ADAPTATION TO THE ENVIRONMENT

The late Samuel Brody wrote, "Physioclimatology, bioclimatology, or environmental physiology, a rather neglected subject, is worthy of cultivation in its own right to furnish an intellectual basis for understanding and controlling the world." [1]

In some of the developing tropical countries the presence of high mountains and fertile valleys provides an almost unbelievable variety of climatic conditions. Plant and animal scientists in all

---

[1] Samuel Brody, *Environmental Physiology. I. Physiological Backgrounds,* Research Bull. Missouri Agr. Expt. Sta. No. 423, 1948.

disciplines have unusual opportunities to explore an infinite number of interrelationships in plant and animal nutrition, physiology, and genetics, and in plant and animal pathology. The efforts of some of the scientists of these countries are directed along these lines. During the nineteenth and twentieth centuries man has generally taken the position that animals should be selected for specific climatic conditions. One of the principal criteria has been capacity for survival under local environmental conditions, and the end result has been the development of hundreds of breeds of cattle, sheep, swine, and poultry. Most of these are of extremely low productivity and little known outside local areas. This technique of selection for small local environments may have been adequate during the past century, but it is obviously not adequate today. Since native livestock are of low productivity as compared with European or North American breeds, there have been continuing attempts to adapt the latter more productive animals to much less favorable environments. Many of these efforts have failed.

As our knowledge of environmental physiology has increased, the causes of failure have become more apparent. In wet tropical areas the problems of high temperatures and humidity, and the accompanying parasite and disease problems, may at first seem insurmountable. All animal functions—milk or egg production, rapid growth, and fattening—are accompanied by appreciable heat production. In ruminant animals, such as cattle, the heat production accompanying digestion and assimilation and high milk production may be greater than the ability of the animal to dissipate the heat to the environment. The animal has no choice but to adapt to such an environment by reducing food intake; milk secretion is automatically reduced, and the genes for high milk production no longer express themselves. If the mature animal has no resistance to the local parasites and diseases, it may become unthrifty and die. Repeated experiences of this type clearly indicate that the importation of superior animals from another environment is not the easy answer.

Fortunately there are excellent climatic conditions in some of the developing nations which permit the fullest expression of the genes for milk or egg production, or rapid growth and fattening, or fiber production. When climate is not a limiting factor, it is obviously more desirable to import and propagate breeds and strains of known productivity than to attempt to select from less productive native stock. From a practical standpoint, however, it may be necessary to improve the native population by systematic crossing with imported sires or imported semen in combination with artificial insemination.

Climate is not the only limiting factor. The importation of dairy cattle capable of high milk production will be of little value if feeding and management practices and disease prevention are not adequate. In many parts of the world there is an extreme shortage of grain for livestock, or the price relations between grain and animal products are such that it is not economically feasible to use grain supplements. This situation is almost incomprehensible to the corn-belt livestock producer. In some countries where grains have historically been channeled into human consumption, an artificial price structure has been established. When the price of grain per unit weight is greater than the unit weight price of milk or meat, obviously little grain can be fed to animals.

While we have made considerable genetic improvement of live-stock and poultry in the United States, we have made equal improvements in nutrition, management, and disease control. Our present levels of milk, egg, and meat production would be unattainable without protein and energy supplementation. Pasture and forage programs are important, both at home and abroad, but they cannot replace adequate grain feeding.

When the local climatic environment is unfavorable, the possibilities of environmental modification must be considered. In some cases the construction of simple types of shade may make the difference between adapted and nonadapted animals. The purpose of shade is simply to reduce exposure to solar radiation. This principle has long been practiced by swine and cattle producers in many parts of the United States where temperatures equal or exceed those in the tropical zone.

It has long been known that some breeds of cattle will not graze during midday when the ambient temperature exceeds 90°F. With modern forage-handling equipment it may prove highly practical to harvest the forage and to feed the cattle in confinement. Practices of this sort are being studied in many of the developing countries.

There are many more complicated and more expensive types of environmental control. If money is not a factor, it is possible to reproduce almost any climate. The regulation of day length by controlled lighting of poultry houses is a standard practice in the United States. It has been widely studied and often adopted as a practice in other countries. The use of supplementary heat for young chicks and pigs has been adopted wherever large-scale, intensive systems of poultry and swine production are in operation.

ANIMAL NUTRITION RESEARCH

Although much effort has been devoted to the determination of the specific protein, carbohydrate, fat, mineral, and vitamin requirements of the various species of farm animals, nutritionists recognize that species requirements vary with sex, age, season of the year, climatic environment, disease status, genetic makeup, and performance standards. It is obvious to all that each species has basic nutritional requirements for growth, reproduction, milk or egg production, work, or the growth of wool. The problem in the developing nations is both a nutritional and an economic one. In some cases adequate nutrients may not be available within the country, in some cases the needs of the human population do not permit the use of scarce nutrients for animals, and in some cases it is not economically feasible to feed animals for even average performance, to say nothing of feeding for maximum performance.

Nutritional research is following the pattern established in the more developed countries. It has been necessary to determine the extent of gross nutritional deficiencies and the means for their correction. Studies have been made of the adequacies of the essential mineral elements in the soil, plants, and water, and the correction of calcium, phosphorus, and iodine deficiencies is fairly well understood. In many areas, however, almost nothing is known about the availability of these important elements. It is easy to recommend that the interdisciplinary approach be used, and that soil scientists, biochemists, plant physiologists, nutritionists, and pathologists cooperate to map the nutritional deficiencies country by country. The trained manpower to accomplish such a gigantic task simply is not available.

Some of the most significant researches are those being carried out jointly by agronomists and animal nutritionists. The possibilities are endless and overwhelming. It is necessary to know what native feedstuffs are available, how their utilization may be improved through the use of grazing systems, how the native crops may be processed and stored for use during unfavorable grazing seasons, and how yields may be improved by the use of fertilizers, irrigation, and other cultural practices. It is a standard practice to study the introduction of new crops, especially alfalfa, clovers, and other legumes, in the hope that they will prove superior to the indigenous plants. In many areas livestock production has been greatly increased following such introduction.

In the United States we have laid great stress on proteins as a limiting factor in efficient livestock production. Although I do not intend to give the impression that some of the developing nations have inexhaustible supplies of cheap protein, it is true that their more immediate need is an abundant supply of cheap energy. In many areas well adapted to corn, animals cannot compete for it with the human demand. In some instances the price of corn has been set by government policy at a level which discourages production beyond that needed by man. In other areas well suited to barley, animals cannot compete with the prices established by the brewing industry, and since wheat and oats are often in short supply, the livestock producer is at a disadvantage.

An efficient poultry industry, for either eggs or meat, requires abundant supplies of protein and energy feeds. In many of the larger cities of the developing nations large-scale poultry farms do exist. They often have first priority on the feed supply and their financial success depends chiefly on the relative prices of grain, eggs, and poultry meat.

In certain areas of many of the developing nations the climate is acceptable or even unusually favorable for dairy cattle. Many of the European breeds are well adapted for these areas, and some excellent herds have been developed from imported stock. The need in many cases is not for better genes for milk production, but for more abundant feed at lower cost. Though many nutritional studies have been, and are being, carried out, it is of little value to demonstrate that high milk production can be obtained by the application of good feeding and management practices if these practices cannot be followed because of economic considerations. It has been demonstrated repeatedly that the production of crops such as wheat, corn, barley, and oats can be doubled or even tripled, and that potential production is even greater. It is discouraging to nutritionists and agronomists to see crop production level off when human needs are met and to observe that pricing structures—either accidental or intentional—limit feed-crop production for animal use. It is imperative that the research programs of the agronomists and nutritionists be broadened to include economic and farm management studies. If regulated commodity prices are intended to restrict livestock production, the livestock research worker will have to reorient his thinking. If commodity prices are accidentally and not intentionally limiting livestock production, the livestock research worker can approach his problems with some hope of solution.

ANIMAL DISEASE RESEARCH

It is an understatement to say that parasites and infectious diseases are the limiting factor in efficient livestock production throughout much of the world. It is a correct generalization that in most areas the data are inadequate to establish clear-cut priorities for the attack on specific disease and parasite problems. It is perhaps more meaningful to describe veterinary research as it pertains to certain stages of the life cycle or certain animal functions.

The infant mortality of all species is extremely high. In the warm, humid areas parasitic infestations are the norm, and even the best preventive and therapeutic techniques are hardly adequate. In many herds and flocks the owners do well to maintain herd size, to say nothing of having a surplus for sale. In all areas enteric and respiratory diseases of the young are a major cause of death. Chemotherapeutic techniques are widely and successfully applied and have done much to reduce the losses of young dairy calves. In less intensive livestock systems, for example in the case of meat-type cattle, there is much less veterinary supervision, and losses may be very high. Wherever large-scale poultry enterprises exist, the problems of respiratory disease, parasitism, and a variety of virus and bacterial diseases must be approached in the same way as in the United States. Failure to do so is economically disastrous, and the poultry pathologist attracts the same attention as he does in Europe or the United States.

Reproductive diseases, although frequently undiagnosed, are widespread. Calf crops of 50 per cent or less are common, and with a few exceptions, routine testing for brucellosis, leptospirosis, or trichomoniasis, or pregnancy diagnosis, is unheard of. The development of large dairy herds near the population centers has been accompanied by both increased veterinary supervision and increased research.

The transmission of brucellosis and tuberculosis to man from milk animals has long been recognized, and there has been a gradual increase of understanding of the need for action. Unfortunately, in many areas, milk sanitation at the farm level can only be described as unbelievably bad. Mastitis is common, permanent mammary damage is a leading cause of cow replacement, and, in the absence of adequate pasteurization, brucellosis and tuberculosis are a constant threat to both the human and the animal populations.

The widespread presence of foot-and-mouth disease in many of the developing countries is not only a deterrent to efficient livestock production, but an important barrier to the export of meat to the United States. Previous experience in the United States and Canada has clearly shown that our cattle are highly susceptible to the disease, and that the most stringent measures must be taken to prevent the foot-and-mouth virus from being reintroduced into North America. The joint effort of Mexico and the United States to check the spread of the disease and to eliminate it from Mexico was a great triumph in cooperative veterinary and diplomatic activity.

A number of the developing countries have modest research and control programs, but the progress toward eradication is painfully slow. Much needs to be learned about the foot-and-mouth virus, about the production of effective vaccines, and about the immunity phenomenon. Even if the vaccine were 100 per cent effective, the rugged terrain of many of the infected countries, the lack of understanding on the part of many of the people, and the constant presence of nondomestic animals as carriers of the disease would make control of foot-and-mouth disease a very, very difficult problem.

The diseases mentioned above are only a few of those which exist. The need for trained animal pathologists, adequately equipped laboratories, an educated livestock industry, and operating funds will not soon be met.

ANIMAL BREEDING AND PHYSIOLOGY RESEARCH

It should not be implied that research in animal breeding and in physiology is of less importance than that in nutrition or in pathology. The results of applied animal-breeding research in the developing countries, however, have not been startling. One of the reasons, perhaps the primary reason, is that the selection studies have been noticeably deficient in quantitative performance data. There have been no large-scale performance tests for milk and butterfat production, for example, and the records which are available are badly distorted by environmental effects. This is not surprising when we consider that in the United States, before 1940, our own milk production data were similarly distorted. Although we have made considerable genetic improvement since 1940, a very considerable portion of the increase in milk production per cow has come from better feeding and management. Many of the milk cattle in favorable climatic areas of the developing nations would show dramatic increases in production if fed and cared for according to our standards.

The selection of meat-type cattle in terms of growth rate, feed efficiency, and carcass quality is not yet widely practiced in the United States and is almost unknown in the developing countries. This is even more true of sheep and swine.

The cattle-breeding programs of many of the developing nations, though lacking in quantitative data, are notable for certain pioneering features. The repeated attempts to propagate European breeds of cattle in the hot and humid tropical areas have certainly demonstrated the complex nature of the adaptation phenomenon. They have clearly shown that the climatic, nutritional, and disease environments are collectively more important than genetic makeup. It has also been shown that some breeds are more adaptable to an unfavorable environment than others, and the crossing of some of these breeds has most certainly strengthened the concept of hybrid vigor.

The use of performance-tested sires in the developing nations has become very popular since the development of artificial insemination techniques. Many large-scale studies in the improvement of native breeds, in the crossing of a wide number of different breeds, and in the development of new types of meat cattle are under way.

It has already been pointed out that some of these countries offer unusual opportunities for research in environmental physiology. They offer similar opportunities for work in artificial breeding and estrual cycle control.

Limitations to Animal and Veterinary Science Programs

It is obvious that the effectiveness of any research program is dependent upon the training and imagination of the research workers. One of the continuing problems of the developing nations has been the failure to separate the husbandry aspects of the animal sciences from the veterinary aspects. There is no question but that the two aspects are closely related and equally important; but it should likewise be clear that the two cannot be successfully combined in a single undergraduate professional curriculum. At best such a training program can be expected to produce graduates who are reasonably competent in both animal husbandry and veterinary medicine. It is not realistic to expect the graduates to be highly superior in both.

To be capable of understanding the complex biological, economic, and social problems of our times, both the husbandman and the veterinary scientist must be well grounded in the basic sciences and the humanities. The husbandman must have additional competence in nutrition, genetics, physiology, economics, and farm management, and must have a working knowledge of agronomy. The veterinarian must have training in depth in biochemistry, pharmacology, microbiology, pathology, and physiology.

As these curricula are separated, it will become even more important to strengthen the communications between teachers, research workers, and those engaged in extension activities. In the typical land-grant university these three functions are combined. It is a generally accepted fact that the teacher will be most effective if he is also a research worker, and the research specialist most effective if he also teaches. In the same way, most extension specialists will benefit by some continued research activity.

In most of the developing nations the research talent, much of it highly trained in foreign universities, tends to congregate in separate experiment stations. This system has proved effective over the short run for the solution of the problems of the day, but it has drained the universities of the very kind of individuals who should teach. New knowledge is the key to progress. The close association of teachers, research workers, and extension specialists is fundamental if new knowledge is to be communicated to others. There is a shortage of trained scientists and teachers even in those countries which consider themselves highly developed, and in the United States we have become increasingly concerned about the loss of scientists from teaching positions and their concentration in research laboratories and in industry. This problem is even more acute in the developing nations, where the pool of trained manpower is much smaller. It is urged, therefore, that the colleges and universities of these nations make every attempt to coordinate the activities of teaching, research, and extension personnel. If the talent which is available is used to its fullest advantage, we may expect the emerging nations to develop their own graduate centers, and effectively to train their own people to solve the important, interesting, and challenging problems which now hinder progress in animal production.

Interactions and Agricultural Research in Emerging Nations

CHARLES E. KELLOGG

Deputy Administrator for Soil Survey, Soil Conservation Service, United States Department of Agriculture, Washington, D. C.

EMPHASIS ON THE PRINCIPLE OF INTERACTIONS accounts for the enormous increase in the efficiency of modern agriculture in the advanced countries since the 1920's. Successful farm managers appreciate this principle, perhaps under different names, more than many other agriculturists.

A few weeks ago, for example, I saw a calculation of the rewards of research on hybrid corn: $60 annually to American producers for each dollar invested! I doubt whether a successful corn farmer would make this error. He would know that without other substantial improvements, in machinery, water control, and fertilizers, the superior germ plasm would have been far less effective. Yet other specialists point to the enormous returns to farmers because of the increases in fertilizer use, forgetting the contribution of the new germ plasm in our crop plants. Between 1950 and 1960 production per man-hour on American farms doubled, primarily because farmers knew how to put practices together in relation to the local kind of soil.

Since success in modern farming depends on capturing the great benefits of interactions among several inputs, not simply the additive results of single improvements, the principle of interactions must be kept foremost in suggesting agricultural systems for the newly developing countries. People in these countries want the abundance and efficiency of our kind of farming. Commonly, however, efforts fall far short of potentials because of emphasis on single practices in research, extension, and demonstration.

Partly because of the low social status of the cultivators in many

81

newly developing countries, some people assume that agriculture is simple. Then, too, many of the local technicians and even outside advisers have narrow points of view and tend to think in terms of single, slogan-like programs emphasizing one or two practices, such as improved seeds, green manures, irrigation, runoff control, pesticides, or fertilizers. Yet any one of these by itself is likely to give only low returns, whereas the right combination of practices for the local kind of soil may give truly enormous increases of 100 to 600 per cent.

TRANSFERABILITY OF PRINCIPLES

Because of highly contrasting natural and cultural environments, one can rarely transfer complete farming systems from an advanced to a newly developing country. Mainly we are thinking about transfers from industrial, temperate countries to agrarian, tropical and subtropical ones. Besides differences in the farming systems, many individual practices are differently handled in the two environments. What can be transferred are basic principles and especially research skills, including methods for diagnosing problems in the field and for designing critical experiments to solve problems.

THE WIDENING BASIS OF AGRICULTURE

Agriculture is broadening in two ways. First, modern farming systems are needed on a far wider range of soils than formerly. After all, the bulk of our literature in scientific agriculture sets forth research results and farm experience in the temperate regions. The kinds of soil and crops in these regions have been studied for a great many years. But landscapes in the tropics and subtropics are older and more varied. Some tropical soils developed under humid climates now have dry climates and sparse vegetation. In fact, there are probably more local kinds of soil in the tropics and subtropics than in all the rest of the world. With a few exceptions these soils had not been extensively studied before 1935.

Secondly, modern agriculture depends increasingly on manufacturing and other services. In all the advanced countries, the savings from an agriculture producing above the needs of farm families served to provide the basis for initiating industry. Industry, in turn, has furnished materials to make agriculture still more effective. In our own country direct farm labor has been decreasing sharply while the output has been increasing. Statistically speaking, much of the labor formerly on farms has moved to towns and cities to manufacture farm production goods and to process agricultural products. We now have in the United States many more off-farm agricultural workers than on-farm agricultural workers. Other advanced countries are seeing similar trends.

In the early development of modern farming, say roughly a hundred years ago, the improvement of agriculture was looked for mainly in the application of science, especially natural science. At that time "farming" was nearly synonymous with "agriculture." This is no longer true. In the newly developing countries, as in the advanced countries, modern, efficient agriculture will depend heavily on towns and cities for production goods and for other services, including food processing.

Basic and Applied Research

I was once taught that basic agricultural research was original research directed toward the discovery of the basic principles governing the behavior of soils, plants, animals, water, and related factors of production. In original applied research it was assumed that the basic principles were catholic and the research effort was to apply them to specific problems. Although these concepts can be useful, they can be misunderstood. Actual researches cannot be classified as basic or applied without knowing the intentions of the scientist. We can hardly imagine one group of scientists busily developing principles which they forward to a separate group that applies them.

I should say that essentially all important, original agricultural research has been directed toward practical problems. Its success is unchallenged. Obviously all steps in research cannot be taken at once. The investigators found that they had to go deeply into research for basic principles in order to reach their objectives. In fact, a high proportion of the principles laid out in modern books

on plant physiology, biochemistry, genetics, soil science, entomology, and animal science was contributed from basic research
done as an integral part of applied agricultural research.

APPLICATION OF THE PRINCIPLE OF INTERACTIONS

The principle of interactions has many applications. We know
that the effect on soil behavior of any one soil characteristic depends on the other soil characteristics in the combination that
makes a soil of a certain kind. That is, we can say very little
quantitatively about the individual effect of the amount of clay,
the kind of clay minerals, the pH, the slope, the thickness of soil
horizons, and so on through a long list. The effect of each one depends on the others. Some soils rich in clay are nearly impermeable
whereas others are highly permeable. Some sloping soils have a
high erosion hazard under cultivation whereas others have a very
low erosion hazard, and so on through all the qualities of soil that
are important to their use for agriculture and forestry.

This same principle applies to combinations of soil management
practices intended to modify or change some of the soil characteristics in order to improve their productivity for crops.

FIELD CONDITIONS ESSENTIAL FOR A GOOD HARVEST

When we combine the plant with the soil we have another set
of important interactions. For example, many seeds used by cultivators have been selected for generations to grow on an infertile
soil with poor water relations. If we add fertilizer and water, the
odds are high that plants from such seeds lack the genetic potential
to respond much to the improvements.

On every acre of soil in the world that has a good crop harvest,
a minimum of seven conditions are suitably arranged in respect
to one another either by tradition or by planning. What we need
to do to maximize the harvest on an acre depends on the interactions of these conditions with one another and with the local
kinds of soil we have to work with.

1. The ideal arable soil has a deep rooting zone with adequate
volume for the storage of water, air, and plant nutrients and for the
extension of roots.

2. A good arable soil is stable in place. Under use it does not slide away or blow away. In the present state of our knowledge we must recognize that some soils cannot be used for crops because we have no combination of practices that will keep them stable and also productive.

3. A good arable soil has a balanced supply of nutrients as needed by the kind and variety of crop, mixtures of crops, or sequence of crops. This means balance among the several nutrients and in the relation of the nutrients to the genetic potential of the crops and the supplies of water and air available to them.

4. Within the rooting zone the soil has both moisture and oxygen as the plants require them. For most soils in the world this means a need for at least some practices for controlling the water, including measures for drainage, flood control, irrigation, and runoff control, commonly in combination.

5. A good arable soil is free of injurious salts or other substances that interfere with the normal relations between soils and plants.

6. The kinds and varieties of crops grown have the genetic potential to respond to the environment as it may be modified by either a simple or a drastic combination of practices. In relation to inputs of production, a crop variety that does best on one kind of soil can do poorly on another kind.

7. The management system includes measures to protect the soils and the crops against insects, diseases, and other hazards. Some of this protection may be bred into crops; some of it is related to tillage systems; and some of it requires special chemical treatments. Weed control, for example, can be handled indirectly or through chemical treatment. And the need for weed control and its timing are intimately related to the other cultural practices.

When we add the animal to this combination of soil, plants, and water, we get another set of interesting interactions. A great many kinds of soil support excellent pastures of close-growing plants. If nitrogen is scarce and expensive, and clovers can grow, we prefer a legume in the pasture. If nitrogen is cheap we may do better to omit the legume. The grazing animal can improve pastures or it can reduce their production enormously, depending upon the physical condition of the soil. For this reason, in certain parts of the world I expect to see more stall feeding and less pasturing because of the much higher volume of forage produced in the absence of the grazing animal.

THE WHOLE FARM SYSTEM

Besides the intimate relations among water, soil, plants, and animals in large or small fields, we must appreciate the important interrelations among these fields. Since most crops give quite unlike harvests from the unlike arable soils that can be developed in the various fields, only at the lowest level of productivity can we expect just one "best" use for any kind of soil. Usually there are several alternatives, and commonly a large number for each kind of soil. For example, on farms with soils that return their greatest output for the input in the form of forage and livestock, the manager has the problem of balancing the total feed supply for the year in relation to some optimum number of animals, or to a combination of cash crops and animals. Then, too, the cost of land preparation and harvesting depends on the size and shape of the fields. The extreme fragmentation of holdings is a big problem in several newly developing countries. A small farm of ten acres can be split into a dozen or more isolated tracts. Such fragmentation makes it impossible to manage irrigation, drainage, tillage, runoff control, and the like efficiently. In large areas of the world, schemes are needed for consolidating such holdings in ways that make fields of practical operating size and that permit efficient village planning of roads, ditches, canals, and terraces. This does not necessarily mean putting all parcels of a single holding together in a block, but certainly fields having similar kinds of soil should be together.

THE OFF-FARM ESSENTIALS FOR MODERN AGRICULTURE

The enormous growth in productivity and efficiency of farming in the advanced countries has resulted from the widening concept of agriculture mentioned earlier. Every advanced country I know about started on the upward road when its agriculture produced well beyond the needs of the farm families. The savings of agriculture formed a basis for getting industry started. Unhappily, some people do not get this idea from a study of only the current economic problems of the advanced countries. They need to go more deeply into their economic histories. It is simply out of the question to expect industry to develop in the emerging nations in the midst of a subsistence type of agriculture with old and inefficient practices.

As industry develops in the advanced countries, products become available to farmers that make possible new systems far superior to the old ones. In the United States and Europe farmers now use increasing amounts of machines, chemicals, and other supplies manufactured in towns and cities. Direct farm labor has gone down proportionally. This process continues.

Of course, in addition to these supplies and the processing of agricultural products, farmers have had the help of research, education, advisory services, technical assistance, and financial services. I should say now that perhaps the greatest emphasis needs to be on education. Modern farming requires operationally literate people. But my subject here is mainly research.

INTERDISCIPLINARY RESEARCH

Perhaps we can all agree that the total research effort in the newly developing countries, especially in the tropics and subtropics, is woefully inadequate to bring forth the enormous potential for food and fiber production. I should also maintain that too high a proportion of the present research in these areas is along narrow commodity or functional lines. Greater emphasis should be placed on general research institutes with good staffs in all lines. In the beginning especially, such institutes should serve as the headquarters for soil surveys and other urgently needed field research. Thus, with both field and resident staffs working together, it would be possible to diagnose the local problems, to select both practices and breeding materials based on research and on experience elsewhere in the world on similar soils, and to set up critical experiments, field trials, and demonstrations that would take account of all reasonable potential combinations.

For the kind of research effort I have in mind I can think of no better example than the Institut National pour l'Etude Agronomique du Congo (INEAC), especially as it operated between 1935 and 1958. But many other examples could be cited, including the developing research institute and graduate school at New Delhi, India.

We can find tendencies not only to set up small, single-practice stations with small staffs, but also to disassociate the research from the teaching and the advisory services. The fact that we have these three together in land-grant colleges in the United States has been highly beneficial to our agriculture. I hasten to add that one can hardly transport this precise organization to another country, but other ways can be found to arrange for the coordination, which is the important point.

Besides arrangements for interdisciplinary research, concentration of staff permits people to work with their peers of the same discipline. In a high proportion of our agricultural research, progress depends upon having competent plant scientists, soil scientists, animal scientists, economists, and so on working together. But for this interdisciplinary research to be effective, these same individuals need the experience of working part of the time with their own colleagues. That is, members of a research staff need to work with people in their own disciplines as well as with those of other disciplines. One scientist by himself, for example, with no one of equal competence to talk to, is likely either to become dogmatic and narrow, or to lose confidence in his own judgment.

To establish advanced general research stations, difficult problems of financing and especially of recruitment must be solved. Perhaps the greatest difficulty is provision for strong scientific work in the field. Many find some sort of social handicap in field work. They prefer to wear white coats in the laboratory. I am not arguing that we have too many laboratories—not at all—but I do emphasize that both the diagnosis of production problems and the fitting together of the many practices to take full advantage of the interactions are most commonly done by scientists wearing rough clothing in the field. Not only must the practices be related to one another, but also the combination must fit the local kind of soil. This scientific work in the field cannot be relegated to the ill trained and inexperienced, if successful results are to be attained.

For a new institute, scientific field studies should precede decisions on location of the institute, and especially of the areas for field trials.

Research and Higher Education

Besides research results, the newly developing countries need well trained agriculturists at all levels in the agricultural system—cultivators, advisory officers, and research scientists. In the United States we have had research, both undergraduate and graduate teaching, and the advisory work in agriculture under the same roof. Not all teachers have taken advantage of the opportunities to use research and problem diagnosis as teaching devices with undergraduates. But the good teachers have.

Up to the present, many of the emerging nations have been encouraged to send students to the advanced countries for training. On the whole, the results have not been encouraging, for several reasons. Only a few professors in the advanced countries can give students from the tropics practice in diagnosing problems outside the temperate environment. In fact, a fair proportion of our teaching in the United States is provincial and even fails to cover the general principles of agricultural systems within the whole country, let alone the rest of the world.

The necessary professional training can be done best locally. Scholars in agriculture from advanced countries, whose students have been successful, can help establish institutes that combine research with both undergraduate and graduate training. Students should live and study in natural and cultural environments like those where they are expected to work. After they have completed their graduate training, and demonstrated their ability to diagnose and to solve problems in such an environment, is the appropriate time for advanced study abroad as needed for special skills.

Each country must count on training its own scientists and engineers. Thus I feel that the highest priority should be given these dual-purpose institutes.

Why the Monograph Thesis?

Interdisciplinary research in agriculture has been emphasized during all my professional life and especially since the general recognition of the enormous importance of interactions within farming systems. We emphasize the team approach to problem diagnosis in research, and in application. Yet even today, during their most important formative years, essentially all agricultural graduate students are required to concentrate on a monograph. We have many excellent opportunities for an animal scientist, a plant scientist, and a soil scientist to work together on a joint thesis; or for a soil scientist and a plant scientist, an economist and a soil scientist, a plant scientist and a biochemist, and so forth.

I hope we do not insist on the monograph system in our work with new institutes in the emerging nations. I can see no valid reason for continuing to insist that agricultural students carry on their graduate work in ways that we ourselves recognize as generally unproductive. They must learn to work with other scientists at some time. Could we not give the graduate deans appropriate forms to provide for two or more students in different fields to use one joint thesis, and thus teach our young scientists to appreciate scholarship in other fields and to understand the principle of interactions through interdisciplinary research?

THE METHOD OF GEOGRAPHIC CORRELATION

Good beginnings on the problems of developing countries need not await the development of ideal general research institutes. We could make better use of our available data and experience than we have, through wider use of the method of geographic correlation based on scientific field study. For a few kinds of soil in the tropics, data usable as a basis for suggesting modern agricultural systems are lacking. But for most soils important data are available. With the organization of this knowledge, including the results of strictly empirical experience, under a uniform system of definition of kinds of soil, a great deal of information can be transferred quickly to entirely new areas once the local kinds of soil are recognized. Through local research and testing, tentative recommendations arrived at in this way can be improved. But until full research and testing services are available, recommendations reached by this method can be far better than current practices. And where facilities are available, one can have a highly useful list of the most likely alternative combinations of practices to test.

SUMMARY

Interdisciplinary research to learn the interactions among farm practices, and the application of combinations of practices in accord with the local kinds of soil, characterize modern agriculture in the advanced countries. The principle of interactions applies in planning a management system for a field or for a farm. The principal research and educational requirements to develop the basis for the efficient agriculture which modern science and technology make possible in newly emerging countries are highlighted.

SEE ALSO: Charles E. Kellogg, Interactions in agricultural development. In *Science, Technology, and Development*, United States papers prepared for the United Nations Conference on the Application of Science and Technology for the Benefit of the Less Developed Areas (Geneva, 1962), Vol. III, *Agriculture*, pp. 12–24. U.S. Government Printing Office, Washington, D. C., 1963.

Education and Development of

Human Resources

The Role of Educated People in Agricultural Development

RICHARD BRADFIELD

Special Consultant, The Rockefeller Foundation, New York, and Professor Emeritus of Soil Science, Cornell University, Ithaca, New York

ARISTOTLE SAID over two thousand years ago, "A lawgiver should direct his attention above all to the education of youth." The more highly developed countries in the world today are those whose leaders have followed this advice, and the underdeveloped countries are those whose leaders have ignored it. Even before the time of Aristotle, scholars were thinking about nature and recording their thoughts and experiences in books. As a result, we have accumulated a great deal of wisdom through the centuries; collective wisdom which is stored in libraries, private and public, throughout the world. Fortunately, this accumulated learning is usually available to all people in all countries, provided they have the key. The key to these great storehouses is the ability to read and understand what has been recorded: to understand the languages in which it is written, not only the different languages spoken in different countries, but the technical languages of specialists in different disciplines—the languages of mathematics, physics, chemistry, and biology, for example. No one man can master all these languages, but a modern nation needs among its people men who can understand most of them.

Fortunately, our leaders in this country believed from the start in the education of youth—*all youth*. We may differ widely on the kind of education, on educational methods, on the amount of education, on who should have the responsibility for education, on who should pay for it, and on many other questions, but there is an almost universal appreciation of the value of universal education in the United States. Until the Civil War, about a hundred

95

years ago, higher education was largely restricted to a few fields: law, medicine, theology, and education. As science developed and its potential for influencing all aspects of our national life, including "agriculture and the mechanic arts," was more widely appreciated, agitation for a broader concept of higher education increased and in 1862 resulted in the passage of the Land-Grant Act. This act, and the later legislation creating the agricultural experiment stations and the agricultural extension service, laid the foundation for our agricultural development. The strong position of our agriculture today would have been impossible without these institutions; for the hundreds of thousands of men they have trained, the research they have done, the auxiliary services their graduates have helped to develop, the techniques they have devised for getting the new information to farmers promptly have been essential to our progress.

The effects on our agriculture can be seen by all. We have an abundance of high-quality food—all we can consume, all we can sell—and still have much left over for the relief of undernourished people in other parts of the world. All this abundance has been produced with less than 8 per cent of our population on farms, and at such a price that it takes less than 20 per cent of the income of the average factory worker to feed his family. All these benefits are parts of the harvest from our investment in education and research, as Professor Theodore W. Schultz and his students have so dramatically proved.

This is neither the time nor the place to analyze these developments in detail. There are, however, a few lessons for the developing countries in our experience.

First, returns from an investment in education and research in agriculture, although very large eventually, do not come quickly, but often require a generation or more for full fruition.

Second, the greatest gains in agricultural production usually do not come from an improvement in a single practice, but from the interaction of a suitable combination of improved practices, as is shown by Dr. Kellogg in his paper in this volume.

Third, agriculture cannot advance alone. There must be a simultaneous development of the industries which supply essential goods and services to agriculture. There are interactions between industries as well as between different sectors of the same industry.

Fourth, large returns from agricultural development are not realized until the farmers responsible for a high proportion of the national production have adopted the improved practices.

Per capita expenditures for education in the United States are probably higher today than in any other country of the world at any time in history. Among youngsters of high-school age (15 to 19), 90 per cent are in school. There are about 4,500,000 young people in our colleges and universities at the present time, and this number is expected to double in the next decade. Even so, there is probably more thinking, more discussion, more planning, and more expansion in education in the United States now than at any time in our history. A commission of national leaders in education have just recently recommended that tuition-free education be made available for two years beyond high school through our rapidly expanding system of public and private junior colleges.[1] This would provide fourteen years of general education. This recommendation is an indication that there are but few if any places in the United States today for the uneducated man or woman. It is the uneducated, in both farm and urban communities, who are unable to cope with the complexities of our modern environment or to take advantage of the opportunities which these new developments place within our grasp. European countries are having a similar experience. They are finding that they do not have enough people trained to the level necessary to man their modern industries. To remedy the situation, many of them are planning to double the percentage of their national income allocated for education.

Our concern with education is not limited to its quantity, but is directed even more to its *quality*. This is one of the most exciting developments of the past decade. Recent studies indicate clearly that our youth have intellectual potentials that have not been fully utilized and developed, especially in our elementary and secondary schools. Results obtained in a few pioneering schools indicate that with the newer methods of teaching many students can acquire in high school a grasp of mathematics and science

[1] *Time*, Jan. 10, 1964, p. 26.

equivalent to that normally attained at the end of the first year in college.

Most underdeveloped countries are beginning to realize the importance of education at all levels and are devoting a higher proportion of their income to it than many of the more advanced countries; but because of their much lower income, the funds available for this purpose are woefully inadequate. Even more serious is the shortage of qualified teachers. This shortage will limit the rate of progress, even when adequate funds are available.

The generalized curves (Fig. 1) showing the frequency distribution of people with different levels of education in an underdeveloped and a more highly developed country (United States; see discussion on a later page) [2] may be of some value in our analysis of this problem of education. The range in levels of education in the two types of country may be quite similar. Each will have some people who are illiterate and each will have some people trained through the Ph.D. level. The curves will differ, however, in most other respects. The functionally illiterate are usually less than 5 per cent of the total population in the more highly developed countries and often range from 50 to 80 per cent in the other group. Sixty-four per cent have at least twelve years of schooling in the United States, in comparison with less than 5 per cent in most underdeveloped countries. At the B.S. and Ph.D. levels, the differences are wider still.

These differences in the level of education of the various sectors of the population concerned with agriculture are of great significance in agricultural development. In a recent study by a committee of agricultural extension workers in the North Central Region of the United States it was found that farmers varied widely in their response to new recommendations growing out of research.[3] Farmers were divided into the groups shown in Fig. 2. At the extreme left is a small group, making up less than 2½ per cent of the

[2] The abcissa in Fig. 1 is labeled "No. years of education (adjusted for initiative + experience)." This is to provide for those all too rare farmers who, as a result of unusual natural ability and self-education through reading and experience, have acquired the equivalent of many more years of formal schooling than they have actually had.

[3] "Adopters of new farm ideas," *North Central Regional Extension Publication No. 13*, p. 4, Chicago, Ill., 1961.

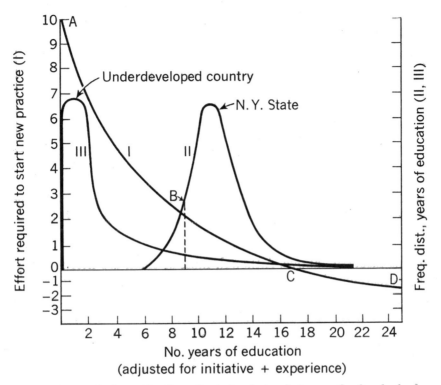

FIG. 1. Curve I shows the hypothetical relation between the level of education of farmers (adjusted for initiative and experience) and the amount of effort (in arbitrary units) required to secure the adoption of a new farm practice. Curves II and III show the frequency distribution of the years of schooling of farmers in the United States (curve II, based on data for New York State) and in a typical underdeveloped country (curve III).

total, who are labeled "innovators." The farmers in this small group have more education than the others. They read more, travel more, keep in closer touch with the research at their experiment station, take greater risks in their farm operations, and have higher incomes. The next group, labeled "early adopters," are not quite as aggressive or as original in their operations as the innovators, but are quick to take up an improved practice when it has been brought to their attention. At the other extreme is a relatively large group, of approximately the same size as the first two groups combined, who are labeled "late adopters" or laggards. This group places more trust in agricultural "magic" and traditional beliefs than do the

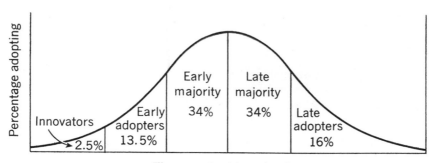

Fɪɢ. 2. Classification of farmers of North Central United States according to the time taken to adopt a new practice. (From *North Central Regional Extension Publication No. 13*, p. 4.)

groups discussed above. Although most of them are literate, they do not read widely nor do they attend educational meetings. Many practices were adopted by the innovators the first year they were available. It took many of the laggards ten years or more to make the same changes. Extension workers admit that they have not yet found techniques which are effective with this large group which makes up about one out of six farmers in the corn belt of the United States, and an even higher proportion in some of the other sections. In time, this group will probably become smaller. Since their incomes will average much lower, some of them will retire from farming and seek employment elsewhere. The young men who take their places will be better educated. As one farmer recently put it, "Lack of education in agriculture is rapidly being corrected by 'survival of the fittest.' . . . Better education of farmers is the key to success."[4]

As was indicated in Fig. 1, most of the farmers in underdeveloped countries have even less education than the laggards in the United States. We do not mean to imply that it is impossible for illiterate farmers, or farmers in the laggard group, to improve their practices. Many of them will do so, but, as the study cited above indicates, it will take much longer and it will require a more costly kind of education. The innovator is looking for new ideas. The lag-

[4] Robert Damman, "Agronomy help farmers need," *Crops and Soils*, Aug.–Sept. 1963, p. 10.

gard resists them. He is suspicious of scientists, and it is only by gaining his confidence and allaying these suspicions that he can be persuaded to try something new. This means that an extension worker cannot reach many such farmers. In our country, which depends largely upon volunteer action, these people do not volunteer and consequently receive little help from the extension service.

I have attempted to epitomize some of these relations in curve I of Fig. 1. It relates the level of education of the farmer (abcissa) to the amount of effort required to get him to adopt a well proved practice (ordinate). It is divided into three sections, A to B, B to C, and C to D. The first section starts at A with the illiterate, isolated, and tradition-bound farmer, the "laggard" referred to above. He *can* be persuaded to adopt a new practice, but it often requires a great deal of persuasion and demonstration. Since he does not read much and often finds it difficult to remember all the details of an operation involving several steps, the demonstration, in which he learns by doing, may have to be repeated two to four times before the farmer reaches the "sustained reaction stage" in which he will continue the new practice under his own steam. Though effective in the long run, such extension techniques are very expensive. One extension worker cannot deal with more than 50 to 100 such farmers. In underdeveloped countries, these farmers operate very small farms, often only 3 to 5 acres. At these rates, one extension worker would be required for each 150 to 500 acres, which is the area of an average farm in the United States. In other words, the number of trained extension workers required in such a system would approximate the number of farmers in the better sections of the United States and would of course far exceed the number of such trained men available in any underdeveloped country.

Education increases one's store of information and, even more important, it increases one's capacity to learn. As a result of both these facts, as the level of education of the farmer increases, less and less effort is needed to teach him a new practice. At point B we reach a level of education, probably in the neighborhood of 8 to 9 years, at which the conventional extension methods evolved in the United States begin to be broadly effective. Farmers seldom adopt a new idea the first time they are exposed to it. Ordinarily it must be brought to their attention several times by different methods and from different sources before they will risk adopting it. As they become better educated, as a result of more schooling or more experience, new ideas from the outside hit them more often and they are more likely to understand, appreciate, and adopt them. Farmers with 8 to 10 years of schooling, or its equivalent, can read the simple instructions given in an extension bulletin, they will subscribe to and read farm papers, they will get ideas from radio talks, and can read timely information sent them in extension news letters by their county agent. They will attend local extension meetings and when in trouble will call on their county agent for help. As their level of education increases, they will become more and more self-reliant, and will depend more on their own independent reading and less on personal help from the county agent. When they reach point C they become "innovators." In section C to D, they will experiment on their own and will become active promoters of agricultural improvements. They will develop contacts with the research workers in their experiment stations and will follow their experiments from year to year. They will call the attention of research workers to new problems needing investigation and will urge their legislative representatives to provide the financial support for necessary research. Most of our top farm leadership comes from this group.

All countries probably have some farmers on all sections of this curve. Countries differ widely, however, in the relative number of farmers on the different sections of the curve. I have attempted to illustrate this with the frequency distribution curves shown in Fig. 1. Curve II, based on data for New York State, represents in a general way the situation in the United States; curve III is typical of an underdeveloped country. We have a few illiterate farmers in New York. Most of the farmers, however, have an elementary-school education (8 years) and an increasing number have had some secondary schooling. The number of high-school and college graduates is rapidly increasing. Quite a few of our leading American farmers have from $100,000 to $300,000 invested in their farm businesses. Not many men with only an elementary education can manage such farms successfully. Our extension specialists report that they have not yet learned how to deal very effectively with the bottom 25 to 40 per cent of our farmers (below B). In other words, our extension system is most effective with the top 60 to 75 per cent. It is not likely to be successful without drastic modification in an underdeveloped country with farmers having even less education than our bottom 25 to 40 per cent. Most countries have, however, a small group of farmers who can be reached by such methods. They are eagerly sought out as cooperators by both extension and research workers.

If we refer again to curve I in Fig. 1, we can see how the job can be done at any level of farmer education. If we have reliable research data and want quick results in production, and *if we have enough good extension workers,* we can increase our investment in extension "campaigns" and subsidies and get returns in a few years. If we do not have enough well trained extension workers, it may be wiser and cheaper in the long run to split our investment between the education of adult farmers by extension techniques and the education of farm youth by the conventional techniques. By increasing the capacities of rural youth to learn and assimilate new ideas, the magnitude of the extension effort required in the next generation can be greatly reduced.

Another argument for this approach is that as agriculture becomes more efficient, fewer people will be required on farms and more rural youths will move to the cities. The cities usually have a surplus of illiterate common laborers but a great shortage of men with enough education for more specialized jobs. The movement from farm to city will be more successful if the migrants are better prepared for urban employment. This is a potent argument for more education for rural youth. Congress has recently provided Federal funds for an expansion of education in some of the more depressed rural areas of the United States with this objective in mind.

Many of our great leaders in the United States have been interested in agriculture, from Washington at Mount Vernon and Jefferson at Monticello in the early days, to Eisenhower at Gettysburg and Johnson at "LBJ Ranch" in recent years. In contrast, the rural youth in most underdeveloped countries look upon farming as a degrading occupation and seek an education as a means of escape from it. Their parents often share this view and are willing to make great sacrifices to help their children through school. If the sons can get the funds and the necessary educational preparation, they will usually prefer law, medicine, or engineering to agriculture. They will usually accept a university training in agriculture only when they cannot qualify for these other fields, and then only if there are good prospects for a government job in agriculture. For, unless his father is a man of wealth, the son cannot, ordinarily, make a very good living at farming. Besides, farming is hard work! "Serf," "peasant," "peon" are terms associated with farming in their countries, and these are not and never have been high-prestige terms.

Most underdeveloped countries have a surplus of people trying to make a living on farms, and they should encourage a migration to urban centers. If they wish to improve their agriculture, however, they should not broaden the gap between farm and city people still further by exporting all the educated and retaining all the uneducated on the farm. If agriculture is to improve, opportunities for making a good living at farming should be available for well educated, ambitious, industrious, pioneering young men. It should be the responsibility of government to provide such opportunities, and the responsibility of the colleges of agriculture to open the eyes of their students to the potentialities and advantages of farming and to prepare them to exploit these potentialities.

Further evidence of the failure of agriculture to attract its needed share of talented youth is shown by the subjects which the youth study when they get an opportunity to go abroad for advanced training. Studies by the staff of the Institute of International Education [5] show that agriculture is not studied by a very high proportion of these students who come to the United States. Figure 3 shows the major fields of study selected by foreign students. Figure 4 shows the fields selected by foreign faculty and scholars. Figures 5 and 6 show the fields in which United States professors and students studied when they went abroad. In no case does this evidence indicate that agriculture will, in the near future, improve its position in the competition for trained leadership with the other sectors of underdeveloped societies. Similar

[5] *Open Doors 1963*, Institute of International Education, New York, 1963.

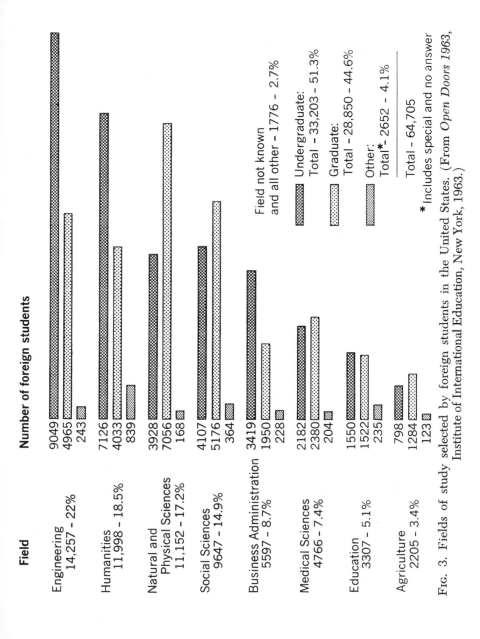

FIG. 3. Fields of study selected by foreign students in the United States. (From *Open Doors 1963*, Institute of International Education, New York, 1963.)

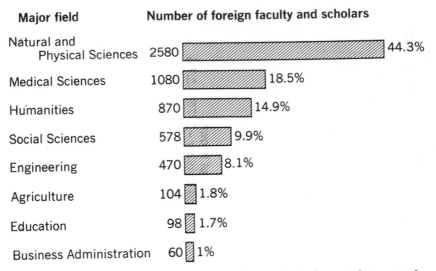

Major field — **Number of foreign faculty and scholars**

Natural and Physical Sciences 2580 — 44.3%

Medical Sciences 1080 — 18.5%

Humanities 870 — 14.9%

Social Sciences 578 — 9.9%

Engineering 470 — 8.1%

Agriculture 104 — 1.8%

Education 98 — 1.7%

Business Administration 60 — 1%

FIG. 4. Fields of interest of foreign faculty and scholars studying in the United States. (From *Open Doors 1963*, Institute of International Education, New York, 1963.)

relationships hold for university students training in their own countries. In Colombia, for example, 60 per cent of the people earn their living by farming, 38 per cent of the gross national product is produced by agriculture, but only 5 per cent of students in the university are studying agriculture.

I shall leave to others the more detailed discussion of how well the training these young people are getting in the United States fits them for doing the jobs which need doing in their home countries. I greatly fear we are not doing as well with this select group as we should. There are many reasons for this, among which are (1) faults in the training and motivation they have had at home before they come to the United States, and (2) the wrong kind of training in the United States.

It seems clear that in most underdeveloped countries, the number of men trained in the agricultural sciences is inadequate and the quality of training both at home and abroad often leaves much to be desired. The influence of these trained men on the agriculture of their country depends also on the efficiency with which their new skills are used. Here again, much of the available evidence is

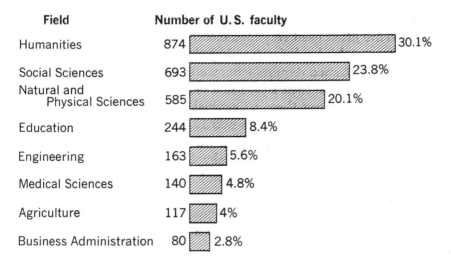

Field	Number of U.S. faculty	
Humanities	874	30.1%
Social Sciences	693	23.8%
Natural and Physical Sciences	585	20.1%
Education	244	8.4%
Engineering	163	5.6%
Medical Sciences	140	4.8%
Agriculture	117	4%
Business Administration	80	2.8%

FIG. 5. Fields of interest of members of United States university faculties studying abroad. (From *Open Doors 1963*, Institute of International Education, New York, 1963.)

Field	Number of U.S. students	
Humanities	8710	54.2%
Medical Sciences	2315	14.4%
Social Sciences	2100	13.1%
Natural and Physical Sciences	881	5.5%
Business Administration	375	2.3%
Education	342	2%
Engineering	259	1.6%
Agriculture	141	.8%

FIG. 6. Fields of interest of United States students studying abroad. (From *Open Doors 1963*, Institute of International Education, New York, 1963.)

discouraging. The talents of the few with a better than average education are often used very inefficiently. As an example: Colombia had 93 normal schools for training elementary-school teachers in 1953. The entrance requirements were usually 5 years in elementary schools and at least 1 year in a secondary school. The number of students entering these 93 normal schools in 1953 was about 8600. The number of teachers was 1110. The number of students enrolled in the sixth and final year was 511, or about half the number of teachers. Two normal-school teachers to produce one elementary-school teacher per year! About 30 per cent of these students were subsidized. The situation is aggravated still further by the fact that 70 per cent of the graduates of the normal schools abandon the teaching profession in a few years for better-paying positions.

The "drop-out rate" is often astounding, even in the elementary schools. For example, in Colombia in 1954 there were about 320,-000 in the first grade in rural schools and less than 500 in the fifth grade. Eighty-one per cent of the rural schools offered a curriculum of 2 years or less, and 94 per cent of 3 years or less. Just how do you use people with from zero to 3 years of schooling to develop a scientific agriculture in a modern democracy? Colombia has three agricultural normal schools with an average of about 15 teachers each. Their capacity for first-year students is about 40 each; the number graduating each year averages about 18, or about *1.2 graduates per teacher*. Not a very high student-teacher ratio by any standard, and prohibitively expensive for an underdeveloped country! The picture varies somewhat from country to country, but is seldom what it should be.

In Kenya, 80 per cent of the children of eligible age, about 1,-000,000, are enrolled in the primary schools. There are only 25,000 attending secondary schools, and of these only about 1000 take the extra two years of sixth form required for entrance to the new $11,000,000 Royal College. As a result, this ultramodern university with a faculty of 109 has only 550 students. In a country where teachers are scarce, some courses have only one or two students.[6]

At the college and university level, there is a common tendency to set up several small, weak, impoverished, often isolated institu-

[6] *Time,* Jan. 10, 1964, p. 27.

tions, instead of pooling the limited supply of human and physical resources and building an institution large enough to be run economically and to provide the diversity and quality essential to a first-class institution.

Many observers have been disillusioned about the role that general education can play in economic development. They will concede that a few educated leaders are needed at the top, but they doubt the value, or at least the indispensability, of education for the masses at the other end of the economic scale. There are many examples which seem to support this point of view. Nigeria is now concerned with what is termed the "school leaver" problem. Rural boys, after completing six years of elementary schooling, are no longer willing to work on their fathers' farms, but go to the cities, where they demand a "white-collar job." There are, however, but very few such jobs for which they can qualify. As a result, they are disillusioned and have become a menace in certain cities. This does not seem to me to be an argument against the education of rural youth, but indicates, instead, that these boys were not getting the right kind of education or motivation. They were not taught the dignity of all honest labor. They were not taught that education carries with it an obligation to perform needed services for society. Their education was not carried far enough to really qualify them to do satisfactory work in the field they hoped to work in. Much education must be geared to the demands of the market. But *education, in general, should not be condemned because some people expect too much, of too little, of the wrong kind.*

Few would argue that some progress cannot be made immediately without waiting for more education of the masses. Most countries have now enough innovators among their people to supply the leadership for an appreciable advance if conditions can be made conducive to change. In practice, the rate of progress is frequently disappointing. In the first place, the educated innovators are usually not as numerous as the short-term visitor from the outside is inclined to believe. Since most of the visitor's contacts are likely to be with this group, they appear to him to make up a higher proportion of the population than they actually do. Because of their scarcity, there is great competition for their services in many different fields. This leads to a rapid turnover and inefficiency. Politics not only accelerates such turnover, but frequently, because of fear and jealousy, causes the removal of capable men from positions of responsibility on the ground of political "unreliability." The more able farmers usually raise better crops, make more money, acquire more land, and hire more laborers. In the case of a social or political upheaval, especially one involving land reform, many of these more capable managers are likely to be liquidated. The kulaks of Russia were her more successful farmers. Their elimination has doubtless contributed greatly to the severity of her food production problems.

Reformers need to develop techniques for accomplishing their political objectives without destroying the talented leaders in the opposition class or party. Instead of shooting or banishing these deposed leaders, the reformers should devise ways for enlisting their services in the development of the country.

Capable leaders in underdeveloped countries are often greatly handicapped by the shortage of well qualified subordinates. Better-trained people are needed at every level. One of the most difficult problems confronting the leaders of education in these new countries is that of distributing their woefully inadequate budgets most effectively among the different levels of education. In a new democracy there is naturally great political pressure for universal primary education, which is seldom carried far enough to be very functional. National prestige calls for universities to train top leaders. The indispensable step between the primary or elementary schools and the university, the secondary schools, is usually the weakest link in the educational chain. A developing country needs thousands of high-school graduates in every sector of its economy. In many countries most of the high schools are private institutions, with fees so high that only the well-to-do can afford to send their children to them. Their primary purpose is often to prepare students for university entrance examinations. Most developing countries need, in addition, hundreds of multipurpose high schools to train thousands of young people for intermediate positions and to form the nucleus for their developing middle class.

The development of an adequate secondary-school system is one of the most difficult problems facing most underdeveloped countries. Since high-school graduates are needed in large numbers in all sectors of the national life, they should be drawn from the brightest children of all sectors of society, and many of them must be returned to the sectors from which they come. They will be needed at all steps on the educational ladder, to supply better teachers for the elementary schools below and to feed the colleges and universities above. Outside the educational field they are needed to supply the expanding demand for better-trained, more intelligent, more trustworthy workers to fill the more responsible jobs in all sectors of the developing economies. No country can realistically hope to hold its own in this modern, shrinking, competitive world unless and until it provides at least a high-school education for a substantial proportion of its brighter youth.

Having already achieved this goal, the more advanced countries are planning for more educational opportunities beyond high school. Educational leaders in the United States are recommending free public education for all qualified youth for two years beyond high school through a system of junior colleges. Unless substantial help is provided in some way for the developing countries, the educational gap between them and the developed countries will become wider instead of narrower in the next decade.

CONCLUSION

Much of the poverty and disease in underdeveloped countries can be attributed to their failure to adopt the lessons of science and apply them to their problems of health, agriculture, and industry.

To do this they must have many men trained in science and technology: scores at the Ph.D. level, hundreds of college graduates, thousands of high-school graduates, and tens of thousands of elementary-school graduates. While most of the Ph.D. training should be done in the more developed countries for the next decade, the training of some of the M.S. candidates, most of the undergraduates, and practically all the high-school and elementary students can be done most economically within the country. This will require, however, many more well trained teachers than most of these countries have at the present time.

Many countries are requesting hundreds of Peace Corps volunteers to teach in their elementary and high schools. This has been and will continue to be of great help, but it is not enough. We in the United States can supply in this way but a small fraction of the number of teachers needed. Each of these countries needs to train thousands of native teachers. This will require scores of well trained, experienced *teachers of teachers* of science for their normal schools, colleges, and universities. Persons with the qualifications required for these jobs are scarce in all countries.

There is, however, one very valuable pool of such men and women available which we can and should utilize. I am thinking especially of the thousands of capable, experienced high-school, normal-school, college, and university teachers who reach compulsory retirement age each year. Many of them, perhaps 5 to 10 per cent, have good health and would thrill at the opportunity for a three- to five-year postretirement career as trainers of teachers of chemistry, physics, mathematics, biology, agriculture, and English in an underdeveloped country in which English is the language of instruction in the high schools and colleges. There is no political dynamite in any of these subjects. In most cases their principles are universally applicable. But little adjustment to the new local environment would be necessary.

I visualize a type of *Senior Peace Corps,* recruited for and largely restricted to this specific job of training high-school teachers of science. The expenditure of a few million dollars a year on such a project, for a decade, would be one of the best long-term investments the United States could make. Nothing we could do would be of more permanent value to the underdeveloped countries. They will appreciate such help, for it will enable them, in time, to stand on their own feet. This is what they want and what we want.

SUMMARY

The nations that are most advanced agriculturally are, in general, those that have made a substantial investment in science and education during the past century. Education is essential at all levels and is an important factor in the readiness with which farmers adopt new practices. The better-educated farmers tend to be the innovators, they read and travel more, follow the progress of research, and assume greater risks in trying new practices.

Where educational levels of rural people are low, the magnitude of the extension effort might be reduced in the future by placing more emphasis on education of farm youth. It is most important that developing nations encourage a fair share of their educated, industrious, and pioneering young men to remain in farming, to ensure progress in agricultural development.

On the basis of the major fields of study selected by foreign students, there is not yet sufficient appreciation of the importance of well trained leadership in agriculture.

In most developing countries the number of men trained in the agricultural sciences is inadequate and the quality of training, at home as well as abroad, must be improved. The limited human and physical resources of the new nations should be utilized in establishing a limited number of first-class institutions.

The large number of capable high-school, normal-school, college, and university teachers in the United States who reach the mandatory retirement age each year, but who are in good health and wish to continue to serve mankind, should be utilized as a "Senior Peace Corps" to teach the teachers of science in advancing nations.

The Rural People of Developing Countries: Their Attitudes and Levels of Education

HAROLD R. CAPENER

Professor, Department of Agricultural Economics and Rural Sociology, The Ohio State University, Columbus, Ohio

NUMBERWISE the rural people of developing countries constitute a very significant proportion of the world's population. Demographers seem agreed that approximately two-thirds of the earth's population reside in developing countries. Of these inhabitants, between 60 and 80 per cent live in the rural areas; thus it would seem that between two-fifths and one-half of the human population of the world can be characterized as rural people of developing countries.

In developing countries the level of formal education is low. This circumstance, perhaps more than any other, acts as a deterrent on the potential rate of development. There is uniform agreement that the greatest resource of a country is its trained human capital. Untrained human numbers may constitute both a burden and a resource. Population control measures daily become more important. The levels of knowledge, skills, abilities, hopes, and aspirations of the people will dictate the rate and degree to which the country can utilize its material, geographical, institutional, and cultural resources.

The rate of literacy in the majority of the underdeveloped countries ranges roughly between 10 and 30 per cent. This means that only about one in eight persons can read or write his name. In the rural areas the rate may be still lower. The pertinence of literacy to development concerns the ability of the people to understand, assimilate, accept, and use advancing science and technology. Lacking the opportunity systematically to gain new experiences, knowledge, skills, and abilities, the typical rural resident of a village in a developing country relies upon and is guided by long-established custom, habit, and tradition.

The level of education of perhaps one-half of the world's population derives not from systems of formal education but from cumulative experiences of an informal nature which add up to their total life experience. This experience is largely related to the daily struggle for sufficient food for existence. Out of this struggle have evolved logical and reliable practices which have faithfully served limited purposes through the centuries. To name a few, there is the practice of leaving land fallow for a season in the hope that it will regenerate its productive capacity; of using a wooden plow which can easily be replaced, repaired, and carried, and can be pulled with limited power; of sowing, harvesting, and threshing by hand; of tenants' mining the resources of owners' land, trying to come out ahead; and of using cow-dung cakes for fuel.

The persistence of such practices in the twentieth century points up the serious nature of the blockade on information, new ideas, and learning which lack of literacy partially imposes. It also testifies again to the validity of age-old principles, such as: man is a product of his total life experience, man is a social being, and man is culturally bound.

The types of attitudes held by rural people in developing countries are largely a function of the cumulative learning of their total life experience. It is not possible for men to know about, think about, or do anything about new discoveries, inventions, or technological advances of which they have no knowledge or awareness. This fact is really brought home as one talks to a village farmer about the possibility of raising one hundred bushels of corn per acre in place of his thirty bushels. The expression on his face and the look in his eye give one the feeling of being almost immoral to tell such fantastic stories. What is accepted fact or truth has to be individually learned, socially accepted, and culturally approved.

The first efforts to introduce hybrid maize in the Punjab in India failed primarily on two counts: first, the biological problems of direct introduction and adaptation of North American varieties; second, social and economic biases having to do with difference in color, appearance, and taste, and with market acceptance, price control, and the handling of a series of complicated multiple practices. In accepting new ideas or practices the given individual has his own attitudes and feelings to sort out; he next has to relate these to an enlarging circle of family, group, and village influences which in turn are conditioned by broader geographic, political, social, economic, religious, and climatic factors.

Let me further illustrate the operational influence of social and cultural ties on behavior and attitudes. In a given village in northern India one finds a fairly uniform pattern of social organization. The social structure of the village is layered by well defined class or caste groupings. Within each group the families are circumscribed and identified largely by occupational pursuits. Upward mobility for a lower-caste or -class male person is best achieved by leaving the village and losing his identity or developing a new one in government service or in a larger urban center. Females may entertain little or no hope of change in class or caste positioning, since they are normally destined to be allied through arranged marriages with families from another village of similar class or caste status.

The people within the village come to know and appraise one another in terms of who they are, what they are, and their relative standing in the social order. The extended family groupings tend to be well defined, and as frequently as not dissensions within and between families arise, sometimes to be resolved and sometimes to give rise to bitter factions or groups whose antagonisms persist over decades.

Village disorganization is as potentially present as village co operation. From a number of investigations we have learned that popular topics of conversation of the village hooka-smoking circle are not the identification of village problems and possible resources to alleviate them, but criticism of a number of identifiable targets ranging from the government to opposing factional groups. The climate for change and ready acceptance of new ideas is not always as healthy as change agents would like to think.

Another feature of attitudes which are culturally derived and sustained is the position and respect accorded elders in the village and in the family. In a recent study inquiring whether cultivators would proceed with projected plans to use commercial fertilizer if they learned that their father disagreed, nearly all replied they would refrain from using the fertilizer and would respect their father's wishes. A very high percentage also indicated that they would be reluctant to use fertilizer if their elder brother disapproved. Attitudes such as these represent a network of interlocking social and cultural influences which when better understood make behavior appear quite rational within its particular context.

Hope for the future lies in education. Education of rural people of developing countries is quite properly identified as the long-range solution; at the same time its effectiveness is perceived to be conditioned by numerous problems. Many of us have seen the plight of young men with foreign training who, upon their return to their home country, have been unable to find a job. At the same time we have seen the same kind of young men return home, obtain jobs, but rapidly become discontented over the level of their pay, their title, their status or recognition. It is well for these young men to express anxiety for suitable opportunities to contribute their new training and skills. At the same time they and their administrators must become more realistic about adjustments in employment, assuming meritorious performance, to make the pay and the working conditions fit the importance of the job.

The problem of attitudinal concern with status, however, pervades far beyond the nationals with foreign training. In fact, the paradox in agriculture is that virtually none of the rural farm boys who go in for higher training in college ever return to their own village or to their own farm to work. Once an extended family decides to set a boy's feet on an upward path of mobility through training and advancement, barring failure, the boy is never permitted either by the family or by the village to return to his former position. The boy must try for some type of salaried service commensurate with his newly acquired status. This pattern, of course, is not unfamiliar in our own culture, especially in earlier times.

Another unhappy outcome of higher education, so far as direct returns to areas like agriculture are concerned, is the reluctance of persons rising in the status scale to work with their own hands. Many programs, demonstrations, and projects fail to reach their potential because of the practice of relying on others with less training or ability to do the actual work. In many instances even the task of conveying instructions or providing supervision is not adequately performed. Quality as a commodity is often obscured by a preoccupation with quantity.

A fundamental approach toward development of functional institutions of higher learning is being sponsored by the United States Agency for International Development. AID in cooperation with foreign governments and different U.S. universities is attempting to establish new institutional patterns in such areas as agriculture, engineering, and education. The main features of such new institutions in India are: curriculum development aimed at more specialization; employment, pay, and promotion of staff on the basis of merit rather than tenure; use of an internal system of examination as a substitute for or supplement to external examinations; integration of the functions of teaching, research, and some system of extending new information and knowledge to relevant users; opportunities for advanced training abroad to enable qualified staff to improve their competence; provision of certain library, laboratory, research, and teaching equipment to ensure better quality of programs; provision of certain advisory staff from U.S. universities to assist in selected subject-matter fields and administrative posts.

These institutions although still in their formative years have real prospects of providing practical, technical, and functional education of the same historical dimension today that the Morrill Act provided for the United States a hundred years ago.

Improved functional education at the college level will help materially. Primary and secondary educational facilities are also vitally needed to provide, within the next few decades, a broader literate base potentially more receptive to improved science and technology. In the secondary schools a heavy emphasis needs to be placed on trade skills and vocational training. Rural high-school-trained boys and girls tend to return to the village, the farm, and local occupations. They can become exponents of and be receptive to expanding scientific know-how.

With regard to adult education, experience drawn from an agricultural district with about 45,000 farmers in northern India has shown a prevailing pattern of farm practice adoption similar to that found in the United States. Nearly every village has a layering of cultivators ranging from large landholders to owners of very small farms. Generally, the small operators, like the group identified as the "laggards" in the United States, have the lowest farm practice adoption index. These are the cultivators who tend to be illiterate, have less operating capital, travel less, do not read, and learn almost everything they know through seeing and hearing. The "innovators" or "early adopters" perform a necessary and valuable function of providing essential learning experiences for the lower-echelon farmers. The so-called trickle-down process of diffusion seems to operate. The important point for change agents to realize is the value of working with farmers so located in the class or caste structure as to be relatively free to try out new practices on a demonstration basis. These should be persons who from the standpoint of social distance are perceived by the lower-echelon farmers as being enough like themselves to attract attention and interest.

In the particular district to which I have referred, responsive farmers have done a remarkable job of accepting and intensifying the use of a "package of practices." One predictable lesson that is emerging is that once a complement of farmers begin to utilize the needed facilities of credit, seed, fertilizer, irrigation, implements, and extension education services, the various departments and agencies of government need to do a major job of overhauling and reorganizing their policy, procedures, and philosophy to keep up with the willing and progressive farmers. Implied here is the need for greater flexibility in policies and procedures of government agencies, to permit realistic response to changing needs and developments of agriculture. Implied too is the need for government officials to develop attitudes and relationships consistent with encouraging and supporting farmers in their vital roles.

SUMMARY

In summary, approximately one-half of the world's rural population resides in the developing countries. These people are for the most part nonliterate. This does not mean they are not intelligent. Their wisdom is born of centuries of struggle for existence under harsh conditions centered on agriculture. The knowledge passed on from generation to generation takes the form of habit, custom, and tradition. These patterns become deeply ingrained in the culture. They are accepted as being right and proper, and are seldom questioned.

In the twentieth century the disparity between the rich nations and the poor nations is becoming visible, communicable, and widely recognizable. The Western nations are faced not only with the problem of providing aid and assistance to developing countries, but with the need to offer material assistance within a framework of understanding and tolerance for patterns of development consistent with the particular conditions prevailing in each country.

The development of the human resources of a nation is recognized as the most important problem to tackle. The solution of all other problems is hinged to the availability and ability of people to activate and manage the affairs of nations. Education of the people is recognized as a direct means of developing the human resources. Educational efforts must be carefully planned to accomplish specific goals and to make wise use of relatively scarce resources.

In developing countries, primary education has long-term payoff implications. Secondary education with a bias for college preparation along with training in practical vocational skills is fundamental. Much of higher education at the college level needs to be critically reviewed from the standpoint of practical utility, job opportunity, and contribution to basic needs of a developing economy. Higher education at present tends to be characterized as classical education for sons and daughters of the class society. Greater opportunity needs to be provided for, and greater emphasis to be placed on, training persons in the technical and professional fields which feed more directly into turning the wheels of the economy. Functional education aimed more at the masses and designed to mobilize and husband the human resources is a definite requirement for short- as well as long-range development.

Attitudes held by rural people condition their thought and behavior. Since attitudes are man-made, they can be subjected to influence and change. Attitudes are best changed when the broader contexts out of which they are formed and receive support are understood. In today's world of opposing and changing ideologies, affluent and nonaffluent societies, the levels of education and the influence of education on attitudes of perhaps one-half the earth's population are of crucial importance and a very germane topic for a conference of scholars.

The Development of Effective Academic Programs for Foreign Students: Curricular, Work Experience, and Social Aspects

DAVID B. WILLIAMS

Director, International Student Office, Cornell University, Ithaca, New York

NEWSWEEK MAGAZINE for April 22, 1963, featured an article on foreign students in the United States titled "Foreign Students: Diplomas and Diplomacy," which described the foreign student adviser as being "among the new breed of campus bureaucrat."

The experience which this member of the "new breed" can bring to the development of effective academic programs for foreign students is that gained as an everyday observer and practitioner, in touch with the full range of academic and interpersonal situations which confront the foreign student. Werner Warmbrunn, president of the National Association for Foreign Student Affairs, opens an editorial in the *NAFSA Newsletter* by stating that "the FSA and his associates in foreign student work, of necessity, are mediators, compromisers and manufacturers of harmony, understanding and friendship. It is our function to bring opposites together, to harmonize conflicts of cultural perceptions and attitudes and to produce as much good feeling as possible." [1]

The development of effective academic programs for foreign students in the United States demands the cooperative efforts of the university's students, faculty, and administration; the student's home government; the educational institutions in the student's homeland; the educational services and officers of the United States Government; any private foundations and agencies that are involved in the exchange of students; and citizens of American com-

---

[1] *NAFSA Newsletter, 15,* No. 2, Oct. 15, 1963, National Association of Foreign Student Advisers, New York. See footnote 4.

munities who recognize the importance of the exchange activity.

This paper, although generally directed to the over-all subject of developing foreign student programs, will emphasize the needs of students from the developing countries. To gain some perspective, let us see who came to study in the United States during the academic year 1962–1963.

Open Doors[2] tells us that 64,000 foreign students representing 152 different countries were studying in the United States in that year. The largest group, nearly 24,000 or 37 per cent of the total, came from the Far East. The next largest group, 11,000, came from Latin America. Africa sent the smallest number of students, 5000, but showed the greatest rate of increase, 27 per cent. Of all the foreign students, 51 per cent were undergraduates and 45 per cent were graduate students. Engineering was the most popular field of study, claiming 22 per cent of the students. Education and agriculture ranked lowest, with 5 per cent and 3 per cent respectively. Forty per cent of the students were concentrated in 32 institutions each of which reported enrollments of 400 or more; and California and New York together enrolled 27.4 per cent of the total number.

Who supported these students? Of the total, 26,000 or 41 per cent paid their own way, and, significantly, 24 per cent of all foreign students, about 15,000, were supported wholly or in part by U.S. institutions. The U.S. Government supported 10 per cent wholly or in part, and foreign governments 6 per cent. Of the self-supported group, 70 per cent were undergraduates. African students were most dependent on outside aid; however, African governments provided support for 20 per cent of their students, and in no other area except the Near and Middle East did the percentage of students receiving government support exceed 5 per cent.

It is predicted that we may have 100,000 foreign students studying in the United States by 1970. Undergraduates from developing countries are likely to continue to increase in numbers until the home country institutions have developed graduate schools able to train the teachers, specialists, and administrators needed to staff the faculties of the undergraduate divisions.

To meet the increasing need for effective programs for foreign students in the United States, we should like to see the work shared

[2] *Open Doors 1963*, pp. 4–9, Institute of International Education, New York, June 1963.

by more institutions. We know that throughout the United States many smaller universities, liberal arts colleges, and teachers' colleges are interested in expanding their undergraduate programs for foreign students, but excellent colleges are often by-passed by students who, as the above statistics show, are drawn to the larger and better-known institutions, for example to the land-grant colleges for technical training in engineering and agriculture. Another factor which bears hard on this problem is that of degree recognition, for relatively few U.S. universities are regarded abroad as worthy institutions. It therefore appears that unless methods are found to bring about a much wider distribution of foreign students throughout the United States, we shall continue to have the largest number of students concentrated in relatively few institutions.

As the pressure for admission mounts, it is encouraging to learn that many colleges, universities, and divisions within them are engaged in serious self-appraisal, looking closely at what they are prepared to offer the foreign student. They also recognize that the offer of admission to a foreign student carries with it a commitment beyond the courses offered.

To emphasize this latter point, I quote from a recent publication: "Programs cannot be strengthened in any meaningful or lasting way unless they are seen in the context of the total international activities, at home and abroad, of any given institution. Those international activities in turn must be placed in the context of the raison d'être of the university."[3] This report goes on to say that "isolated foreign student advisers or faculty may be able to initiate some scattered improvements but the institution will fail both to grasp its opportunities and to meet its responsibilities in the absence of consistent definition and support from the top administration." The acceptance of a foreign student is an acknowledgment that the institution is concerned, not only with its academic offerings, but also with the social environment of the student and the provision for adequate orientation and counseling.

Any university committee charged with the responsibility of reviewing its entire international program will be encouraged by the extensive research and writing on the subject that has come forth since 1955. The subject of foreign students comes up for discus-

[3] *The College, the University, and the Foreign Student*, p. 1, Committee on the Foreign Student in American Colleges and Universities, New York, 1963.

sion at some point in virtually every conference sponsored by higher educational associations or agencies. In 1963 the National Association of Foreign Student Advisers and the Institute of International Education jointly produced a publication entitled *Research in International Education* which notes 112 research studies recently completed or in progress.

The National Association for Foreign Student Affairs [4] is now engaged in a three-year field service project sponsored by the Bureau of Educational and Cultural Affairs of the U.S. Department of State to assist colleges and universities actively attempting to develop more effective programs for foreign students.

SELECTION OF STUDENTS

When an institution has decided what it can effectively offer, it can then direct its energies toward the selection of those students who will be most likely to succeed. This, of course, puts an enormous, time-consuming burden on the admissions personnel, who, realizing that there is so much at stake, must take advantage of every admissions tool at their disposal. They must establish criteria for admission to any college department or division, and then make them stick. Our case study files reflect the results of hasty decisions on admissions. Careful selection of students is *sine qua non* to the development of any effective academic program.

The following quotation indicates the seriousness of this problem.

Perhaps a third of the 58,000 foreign students in American educational institutions in 1962 were thoroughly screened to make sure they had the academic preparation, the language proficiency, and the financial support necessary to a successful study experience. Another third were partially screened at some point in the exchange process, and a final third probably had no screening at all. Thus between one-third and two-thirds of the foreign students coming to the United States today are in some degree deficient in knowledge of what they will find, where they will find it, what preparation they will need, and how much it will cost. In extreme cases they are without funds, without insurance against illness, without sufficient command of English, and without academic

[4] On January 1, 1964, the name of the National Association of Foreign Student Advisers was officially changed to National Association for Foreign Student Affairs.

preparation to undertake study at the level they propose. In less extreme cases they have some funds and at least minimum preparation, but are enrolled at whatever institution that admitted them or offered financial support without regard to the institution's ability to meet their needs or those of their country.[5]

Given the basic requirements (intellectual equipment, language proficiency, and freedom from extreme financial concern), we may now ask, What sort of individual should we encourage to come?

Although there are educational needs at all levels, there is a considerable body of opinion which holds that our selection procedures should give priority to students from developing nations who have what might be called a "social reform attitude" or a "service-oriented outlook." Clifton Wharton states:

> Respondents with overseas experience feel strongly that there is need to send students for [United States] training who have a greater desire to serve their own agriculture. These persons say that the present levels of development in under-developed areas make it necessary to concentrate greatest attention on those individuals with service-oriented motivations. This group does not say that such countries could not make use of some professionals with training in more advanced techniques indirectly related to farm service; rather, the feeling seems to be that the majority of under-developed countries are not yet ready to make full utilization of persons with such skills.[6]

This does not deny that the first consideration must be that of serving the educational needs of a wide range of individual students. It only suggests a priority where choices have to be made.

Another point should be made about the question of financial commitment. *Open Doors 1963* for the first time had figures on the financial support provided to foreign students by American colleges and universities.[7] Their figure of 24 per cent, or 15,000 students, supported by U.S. colleges does not tell the whole story, for a cost-of-education factor is involved that every college and university, state supported or private, knowingly and willingly assumes

[5] *A Foreign Student Program for the Developing Countries during the Coming Decade*, p. 2, Committee on Educational Interchange Policy, New York, June 1962.
[6] Clifton R. Wharton, Jr., *The U.S. Graduate Training of Asian Agricultural Economists*, p. 37, Council on Economic and Cultural Affairs, Inc., Carnegie Press, New York, 1959.
[7] *Open Doors 1963*, p. 8, Institute of International Education, New York, 1963.

for every student it admits. Improper selection can only result in boosting this cost-of-education factor because of the special attention and services required in trying to work out the student's problems.

Earlier I mentioned that 41 per cent of the students coming to the United States in 1962–1963 paid their own way. This "unsponsored student" poses some special problems in selection, in contrast to those students who come to us recommended and screened by reliable admissions representatives of governments, foundations, or private agencies. These "screeners" are people (usually in the student's home country) who, we have learned by experience, can be relied on to recommend well qualified students. Now, the "unsponsored student" may be just as highly motivated, as well prepared, and as intelligent as the sponsored student, but how do we really know? Unfortunately, we do not yet have enough such qualified admissions personnel abroad. However, we can be encouraged by some recent developments.

The Bureau of Educational and Cultural Affairs of the Department of State has been increasingly aware of the growing numbers of unsponsored students coming to this country, so it has recently appropriated funds to expand orientation opportunities for these students.

The development of the new Program for the Testing of English as a Foreign Language (TOEFL) will, it is hoped, represent a real breakthrough in the overseas testing for proficiency in English. This program, to be administered by the Princeton Testing Service, was made available in February 1964. Quoting from the TOEFL brochure, "This battery of tests will examine a wide range of English proficiency and yield meaningful (reliable) subscores in addition to total scores. It is anticipated that the resulting profiles will significantly improve the existing means of predicting general academic success and will greatly assist in the planning of programs of study including, where appropriate, further instruction in English. It is *not* intended that these test scores should constitute the sole criterion of admission to an institution." [8]

A third encouraging development is the expansion of the over-

[8] *TOEFL: A Program for the Testing of English as a Foreign Language.* The program is sponsored by the National Council on the Testing of English as a Foreign Language and associated with the Center for Applied Linguistics of the Modern Language Association of America, Washington, D. C.

seas admissions counseling and evaluation services of the Institute of International Education (IIE), which, working in close cooperation with the education authorities of the countries in which it operates, should be able to provide valuable information for screening the unsponsored applicant. The IIE program uses the judgment of well qualified United States personnel who can assess, by means of test and interview, the relative fitness of the student for study in the United States. The program deserves the support of the universities and colleges, for its cost surely cannot equal that of trying to undo the damage resulting from the admission of a poorly selected student.

The overseas admissions officers should be able to evaluate certain qualities of a candidate which would not be apparent on a written application. A few might be: (a) the level of maturity and sophistication of the student; (b) his travel experience and time away from home and family; (c) his actual proficiency in other languages; (d) the time he may have spent with persons from the United States; (e) the orientation to the United States he may have had or may be expected to have by the time he comes to this country; (f) family circumstances or pressures that might adversely affect him away from home; (g) his motivation.

ORIENTATION

Having accepted the student for admission, the university or college which strives for an effective foreign student program must next turn its attention to the matter of orientation. Here again we must emphasize that careful selection will determine the kind and amount of orientation needed. The Committee on Educational Interchange Policy suggests five goals for orientation:

1. The basic problem facing any newcomer to a strange land is to find his way through the "cultural maze."
2. To correct misconceptions about the people and countries involved in interchange.
3. To increase facility in the language of the host country.
4. To provide factual information and practical guidance.
5. To provide meaningful experiences and personal contacts.[9]

[9] *Orientation of Foreign Students—Signposts for the Cultural Maze*, pp. 3–5, Committee on Educational Interchange Policy, New York, June 1956.

Orientation, by definition, is the determination or sense of one's position with relation to environment or to some particular person, thing, field of knowledge, or principle. This is an attempt to acquaint oneself with the existing situation. An orientation program should not be expected to do too much more than point the way for the individual to "do it himself." Ideally it should lead him to the tools and associations which will enable him to gain the most from his academic and social experience while in the host country.

Those who would develop effective orientation programs should be reminded that "orientation must be viewed, not only as a preparatory undertaking, but as a continuous psychological process, at least throughout the early part of the visitor's stay" and that "it is desirable to offer those facts, ideas, and experiences which at a given time are most likely to seem relevant." [10]

One of the conditions that orientation aims to alleviate is "culture shock." "It is a state of relatively acute anxiety. It is caused by the student's inability to satisfactorily resolve the problems that confront him when he finds himself faced with the problem of making sense out of two sets of often conflicting values, customs, beliefs, and rules of behavior. He finds satisfying communication very difficult. Often he does not have a clear understanding of his new personal relationships. It is small wonder that he frequently lives, for a time, in a state of almost continual anxiety." [11]

We shall never eliminate cultural shock entirely, nor should we be distressed by the fact that we cannot. "Such shock may well be a necessary prelude to true mutual understanding. For the Asian does not know America until he sees both crowded city and hospitable village and encounters Americans rude and gracious, bigoted and tolerant. He must glimpse slums as well as Cadillac-filled driveways. The American cannot know Asia—or one country of Asia—until he, too, encounters both philanthropist and beggar, squalor and splendor." [12] Although we know that culture shock is inevitable, we should nevertheless continue to help the student cope with his new environment.

[10] *Ibid.*, pp. 10–11.

[11] Gerald Shattuck, "Culture shock and your foreign student program," paper written as part of a doctoral dissertation in rural sociology, Cornell University, 1962.

[12] *East West Center News*, 3, No. 3, Sept. 1963, Office of Public Information, East West Center, University of Hawaii, Honolulu.

There is another aspect of orientation that begs for more attention: that of preparing the student for re-entry into his home culture after completion of his academic program. To anticipate re-entry, the U.S. Department of Agriculture and the Agency for International Development have organized communications seminars, held just before the participants depart from the United States. The students are given an opportunity to reflect upon their U.S. training and experience, and are stimulated to think about applying what they have learned to the conditions they will meet at home, and about their own reception as they try to effect change among their people. More activity of this sort would be particularly helpful to those who are returning to work in developing countries. Perhaps those responsible for orientation programs could also give attention to the development of re-entry seminars.

THE CURRICULUM

Assuming that a qualified student has been selected and invited to our university, and that we are providing proper orientation, we must now consider the curriculum. Again I want to emphasize the key roles played by the academic adviser and the foreign student adviser in the successful development of any program for any foreign student. Theirs is a cooperative role of prime importance.

Our title, "The Development of Effective Academic Programs for Foreign Students," does not rule out the development of special courses or non-degree programs for certain groups of students, but, if a foreign student plans to earn a professional certificate or degree, we must make sure that the program we offer him assures him of meeting the requirements for the same degree as that earned by his U.S. counterpart. Professors responsible for recommending this degree need have no qualms about applying the same standards for all students.

Those who have given considerable thought to the development of the curriculum, question whether universities should develop special courses for foreign students. Such courses may be useful for orientation. Michigan State University observes:

Overseas students who enter at the graduate level specialize from the start in their chosen field. Accordingly, they may spend a year or more in the United States without learning much about American agriculture and how it developed, the role of the land-grant system, the nature of the extension service, etc. Such students return home having little knowledge of the agricultural system of the U.S.

An attempt to remedy this situation was undertaken on a trial basis through a 3-credit course at the 400 level in *American Agriculture for Overseas Students* during the fall term of 1962. This course included lectures on American agricultural history and development, modern technology in agriculture, the land-grant college as an institution, types of farming, marketing, processing, the political structure of agriculture and government agricultural policy. In addition to the lectures, the students were required to survey the experiment station literature in a specific field of their choice. [13]

When we try to develop special courses for foreign students in strict subject-matter areas, however, we face additional problems. There may be a shortage of qualified teachers for special courses, and overhead costs are very high. Special courses may tend to remove the foreign students from contact with American students and thereby depreciate one of the basic values of the exchange program.

If we do not develop special courses, then we must try to improve the academic counseling of foreign students, so that they can be directed to select appropriate courses from those available.

New curricular vistas open up for the foreign student when he finds himself confronted with the veritable cafeteria of course offerings. An effective academic program should have enough flexibility so that the student can take advantage of curricular offerings which have relevance and of which he may have been unaware before he arrived. A young student of architecture told me that he was encouraged by his professor to enroll in a psychology course devoted to the study of perception. Allied to architecture? Certainly, but our student was completely unaware of this opportunity until it was pointed out to him—a good illustration of the virtue of curricular flexibility leavened by good academic counseling.

Special programs in agricultural development, such as those at

[13] *The Report of the International Committee for the College of Agriculture,* Michigan State University, East Lansing, Mich., Mar. 1963.

the University of California at Davis and those at Cornell University, which are designed to prepare personnel for foreign service in agriculture, lend themselves very well to the needs of foreign students, and these same foreign students can bring an added dimension to such seminars.

The Committee on Educational Interchange Policy suggests that "the larger the volume of foreign students and programs, the more desirable it is for an institution to concentrate on certain geographic areas in which it has developed certain competence and special materials, or in certain fields of study within broad geographic areas." [14] The area studies approach facilitates selection, pre-departure orientation, and directed orientation after arrival. The faculty is aware of the kind of "cultural baggage" that the student brings with him, so that each student finds an environment of understanding and being understood. The area studies program recognizes the inherent values in comparative education. The chief objection to such a program is that it may tend to restrict the foreign student to the same group of Americans.

WORK EXPERIENCE

Another problem which demands our attention is that of providing suitable field experience and practical training for the foreign student. In academic programing, field experience generally precedes the award of the degree and is tied in with the data-gathering aspect of the student's research topic. When we speak of practical training we refer generally to the kind of work that a foreign student may engage in after he has received his degree.

Field Experience

It would seem most important to give more attention to field work research topics that relate to the student's home problems, so that he can return home to collect his data under direction of a competent field work supervisor. Professor John Mellor of Cornell comments:

[14] *A Foreign Student Program for the Developing Countries during the Coming Decade,* p. 13, Committee on Educational Interchange Policy, New York, June 1962.

In the rural social sciences, field experience largely involves working with data collected from farmers. The data collection process itself is an important part of the research experience. Frequently cultural and language problems make it difficult to incorporate foreign students into field research in U.S. areas. Even where this is possible it does not provide as meaningful or useful an experience as field experience in the home situation. This is particularly true since field research experience at home would for many a foreign student represent his first intimate contact with his own agriculture.

Thus it is desirable that field experience be provided in the home country. A potentially valuable sequence is for the student to develop his background in theory and methodology in the United States, outline a thesis topic, return to his home country to collect data and then return to the United States for analysis of the data under close supervision of supporting faculty who know his situation.

The costs of such a program are largely those of an additional round trip to the student's home region and a share of the travel for a faculty supervisor. The latter cost can normally be spread over a number of students. In any case, these costs are small compared to the total cost of a doctoral degree or of the benefits obtained. An important additional benefit from such a program is the body of badly needed research knowledge pertaining to low-income countries which will come out of carefully directed graduate research projects.[15]

Some universities have established programs that incorporate this approach in area studies programs and in contract programs with universities in other countries.

Practical Training

The present regulations set by the Immigration and Naturalization Service provide that foreign students may apply for permission to undertake up to eighteen months of practical training after finishing their study program. Of course, there are instances in which "practical training" turns out to be simply a job that enables the student to remain up to eighteen months longer in the United States. One might argue that any kind of post-academic work

[15] John Mellor, "Professional training in agriculture for foreign students—Role, problems, and improvements," in *The Professional Education of Students from Other Lands* (Erwin T. Sanders, editor), Council on Social Work Education, New York, 1963.

experience will be of value to the student, but we must be more concerned about the appropriateness of the work experience. In a number of instances it would be in the student's best interest to go home rather than to take a job. Many of us who have been in touch with this problem realize that there are a great many graduate students who, because of the pressures of finishing their theses or study programs, have not had time to locate satisfactory practical training, and therefore search frantically at the last moment. Student advisers should anticipate this problem and help explore appropriate practical training opportunities. Counseling and guidance in the early stages of the student's career should encourage him to look ahead to the kind of work experiences that might benefit him. Proper practical training placement should be tied in with the student's total educational planning.

In two recent surveys of foreign student alumni, one at Cornell and another at Michigan State, an evaluation of practical experience was sought. In Donald G. Green's follow-up study of alumni of Cornell University,[16] a pressing need for more opportunity for practical experience was noted. From this we might gather that we have tended to underrate the value for students while they are in this country of practical training or work experience which will have relevance to the conditions they will have to work with at home. They need to put the broad principles into a practical frame —to see how things are done, and to pick up methods and techniques in the daily give and take of a workaday situation.

Summer vacations offer some opportunities for students to obtain practical training, but in most cases the summer job is strictly a money-earning proposition.

Most placement offices are not geared to work with the problems posed by the job-seeking foreign student; however, there have been some fine results when a trained placement person has tried to match the foreign student with the appropriate job. Sometimes academic advisers, foreign student advisers, and placement officers may find that the most beneficial practical training experience exists in a third country.

---

[16] Donald G. Green, "An analysis of the characteristics and satisfactions of foreign alumni while in residence at Cornell University," unpublished doctoral dissertation.

SOCIAL ASPECTS

The foreign student's social experience is bound to have a profound influence on all aspects of his sojourn in the host country and will condition his relations with the people of his own country after his return. To assess a social program for foreign students, we need to know the student's expectations.

Donald Green [17] found in his study of Cornell foreign alumni that his respondents indicated that they wanted more opportunities to mix with American students. They thought there should be more organized programs for people-to-people contacts, and they wanted more opportunities to meet and know American families.

Because the foreign student wants to know us better, a program should aim at finding avenues through which natural and meaningful contacts can be made. The office of the foreign student adviser, with its variety of contacts, is a logical starting point, and it must consider both graduate and undergraduate students. I think there are four main avenues of approach: (1) housing, (2) departmental efforts, (3) student organizations, and (4) community organizations.

No one would deny that the student's housing is a critical factor in his adjustment to life and study in the new environment. A number of people concerned with the welfare of foreign students maintain that a college or university should not admit foreign students for whom decent housing accommodations cannot be guaranteed. By "decent" they mean not just safe and sanitary, but also well located, with ample opportunity for easy association with other students. Housing must have variety to satisfy the needs of graduates, undergraduates, men, women, and couples with young families. Single rooms should be available for those who need to work alone. Opportunities to room with Americans who welcome such an arrangement should be available. There should be provisions for students to cook their own meals. We could list many more, but one of the main considerations should be that housing does not isolate the foreign student from contact with Americans.

[17] *Ibid.*

The foreign student office can determine a student's needs and can cooperate closely with the university housing authorities to see that the student is in a happy housing situation.

The student's academic department, in which he may be working in close professional association with U.S. graduate students, can do much to promote friendships. Faculty advisers, aware of the importance of these associations, can assign common work space to American and foreign students who may be expected to work well together.

American and foreign student relations are fostered through student organizations, but much more can be done on most campuses. American students must be encouraged to take the initiative in introducing the foreign student to those groups that may hold some interest for him. Foreign student advisers can assist U.S. student groups who are endeavoring to work out ways and means of bringing the foreign student into the main stream of college life.

The expanding interests of those persons we have come to call the "community hosts" and the contribution they are making to the life of the foreign student off the campus simply cannot be overestimated. Family opportunities range from the home stays provided for some students through organizations like the Experiment in International Living, to the local host-family programs of civic groups in towns and cities throughout the land. Foreign student offices and community organizations are continually working on carefully conceived community programs, which are enabling large numbers of foreign students to see the "inside of America."

SUMMARY

I have discussed the development of effective academic programs for foreign students, and out of this we might be able to construct an ideal situation, if we allowed ourselves the luxury of some basic assumptions. Central to any thinking or planning would be the recognition that we should not be any less concerned for the foreign student's intellectual and social experience than we are for that of his U.S. student counterpart. We should assume that this student has satisfied all requirements for admission to a particular college and that its academic offerings are what he needs; that he has demonstrated special ability in those areas which will demand most of him, and that if he comes from a non-English-speaking country he can talk and think in English; that he is financially prepared and has ample time to complete his work. If these conditions can be met, we shall expect to assist the student in finding appropriate practical training on completion of his studies, and finally we shall be gratified if he returns to his home-land motivated to put his education and energy to work in the growth and development of his country.

Establishing Indigenous Institutions

to Serve Advancing Agriculture

Developing Agricultural Institutions in Underdeveloped Countries

F. F. HILL

Vice President, International Programs, The Ford Foundation, New York

AGRICULTURE IS CARRIED ON within the wider economy of a country, and its development is influenced by activities and national policies in a wide range of fields—general and technical education, health, transportation, land tenure, taxation, monetary and credit policies, and so on.

But even if the wider environment is generally favorable to agricultural development, four conditions must be met at the local level if production is to be substantially increased:

First, provision must be made for developing locally adapted varieties of crops and improved cultural practices which, if adopted by farmers, will increase yields by significant amounts. This calls for systematic research and experimentation.

Second, improved seeds, fertilizers, pesticides, and other supplies and equipment required to put recommended practices into effect must be locally available when needed. This requires an effective system for production and distribution of farm supplies and equipment.

Third, suitable forms of agricultural credit at reasonable cost must be provided, since modern agriculture, like modern business, needs access to credit if it is to operate effectively. This applies to small-scale as well as large-scale agriculture.

Fourth, individual farmers must be convinced (*a*) that recommended practices will in fact increase production on their farms, and (*b*) that it is to their advantage to adopt them. This calls for an effective extension service and national policies that make it worth while for farmers to accept such risks as may be involved in adopting new practices.

141

At the present time few developing countries effectively meet one, much less all four, of these requirements. In contrast, the United States and Japan are outstanding examples of countries that are well organized for agricultural production. In the United States, the typical farm business is relatively large and capital-intensive. In contrast, in Japan it is small and, despite developments since World War II, still labor-intensive. However, both countries are covered with a network of agricultural research centers and experiment stations with highly trained staffs that have produced improved crop varieties and management practices suited to the areas they serve. The cumulative effect of these activities over the years, combined with generally efficient systems for production and distribution of farm supplies, good agricultural credit and marketing systems, land tenure arrangements that provide incentives to produce, and favorable cost-price relations since World War II, has enabled both countries to achieve spectacular increases in production. Taiwan is another country that by following the lead of Japan and the United States has achieved a high level of production.

If developing countries are substantially to increase agricultural production on a sustained basis, they too must provide the institutions, facilities, and services that make it possible for farmers to adopt improved practices, and incentives that will induce them to do so. What are some of the major organizational problems that confront a developing country engaged in such an undertaking, and foreign assistance agencies trying to be of help? My list includes (1) development of educational and training institutions; (2) development of adequate agricultural research institutions and experiment stations; (3) development of effectively functioning supply lines, including a supply of credit, and of storage, transportation, and marketing facilities; (4) development of incentives to encourage increased production; (5) development of an effective extension service. A book could be written on each of these topics. I shall confine my remarks to pointing out a few major problems as I see them, particularly as they bear on the job of organizing within the United States to provide technical assistance in developing countries.

Development of Educational and Training Institutions

It is now generally recognized that economic development is in large part a matter of human and institutional development—of developing people, and developing institutions through which they can work effectively. This is not to say that capital and other ingredients of development are unnecessary or unimportant. But it is clear that lacking trained people and effective institutions, natural resources are likely to be underutilized and capital wasted.

As Professor Richard Bradfield, Professor Theodore W. Schultz, and others have repeatedly emphasized, the education and training of people for agriculture is as important as the education and training of people for business and industry. The United States and Japan are examples of countries that for years have emphasized general, technical, and professional education at all levels. They also are examples of countries that have achieved high levels of agricultural production. There is no doubt in my mind that there is a strong cause-and-effect relation there. This also applies to Taiwan, a country which has made great progress in recent years in increasing agricultural production.

Most of the persons required to staff a country's educational and research institutions, governmental agencies, business concerns, and industries have to be trained at home. A few can be trained abroad, but the number will always be small in relation to total needs, even in a small country. This applies not only to elementary, secondary, and college education, but to graduate training as well, particularly to the level of the master's degree.

The number of highly trained persons required fully to develop a science-based agriculture is commonly underestimated by a wide margin. Professor Bradfield has pointed out that since World War I colleges of agriculture in the United States have been graduating from 6000 to 10,000 persons each year, or well over 300,000 since 1920. This is an average of one graduate for every ten or eleven farms in the United States in 1960. Substantial numbers of these graduates have gone on for postgraduate work. Though I would not suggest that developing countries desiring to reach high levels of agricultural production must first turn out agricultural graduates and postgraduates in like proportion, it is nevertheless true that widespread education in the United States, and the large number of persons trained in agriculture and related sciences, are directly related to the high levels of agricultural production achieved in this country in the past half century. It is also true, in my opinion, that many developing countries do not yet realize the size of the investment they have got to make in education if they are to double agricultural production. In addition to facilities for general education, even relatively small countries are going to have to have their own agricultural colleges, experiment stations, extension services, and specialized agencies concerned with agriculture. Large countries are going to require a number of colleges, experiment stations, and specialized agencies and extension services of appropriate size.

The principal way in which the United States or any other highly developed country can help a developing country meet its trained manpower requirements is to assist with the development of educational and training institutions in the developing country. The development from scratch of an effective educational and research institution in an underdeveloped country is a long, slow business. Back in the 1920's I remember hearing Dr. J. Lossing Buck, then working in China, make the statement that to establish a new subject-matter department in a university in a country like China required from ten to fifteen years. I did not understand the implications of his statement at the time. I now do.

With few exceptions, what we in the United States have been trying to do in the developing countries is help with ten- or fifteen-year jobs of institutional development using personnel on one- or two-year appointments. It has not worked very well. We would not think of trying to develop a new department in one of our own universities by appointing a department head and staff on a one- or two-year basis. We would feel in most cases that a minimum of five years was essential to success. And yet we continue to send missions overseas, to undertake more difficult assignments, consisting of persons on one- or two-year appointments.

Having been on the university end of this type of operation, I am fully aware of all the difficulties involved in trying to make personnel available for longer periods of time. But difficulties at home do not solve problems abroad. If we are seriously concerned about trying to improve the quality of the job we do overseas, we have got to find some way to make at least a few first-rate people available for longer periods of overseas service than has been customary in the past. This applies particularly to project leaders. It takes at least one year, and sometimes longer, to learn all the ins and outs of a local situation, acquire the complete confidence of host-country personnel, and develop really effective working relations with them. Deducting vacation and travel time from a two-year appointment leaves too little time to do a really effective job in many situations. However, given a good project leader on a five-year appointment, effective use can be made of other persons on shorter appointments, assuming they are competent and suited for overseas work.

Needs differ, of course, among institutions receiving assistance. The need for foreign personnel on assignments of more than two years is particularly acute in the case of a country with little trained manpower of its own that is starting a new institution from scratch. Under such circumstances a certain amount of responsibility for day-to-day operations as well as for providing advice on policy questions usually has to be assumed by the project leader. Reasonable continuity of leadership is essential to success under such circumstances.

How can the problem be met in the case of United States universities engaged in overseas activities? Let me briefly describe three recent developments which seem to me to point in the right direction.

Harvard University has been providing advisory services in the field of economic planning and administration since 1954. In 1961, an organization called Harvard Development Advisory Services was set up. This organization plans to employ on long-term appointments up to ten so-called development advisers, mostly economists, who are interested in spending part of their professional careers overseas. Selection is made on the basis of professional competence and competence to serve as a team leader. Additional staff consists of long-term advisers recruited for overseas assignments of eighteen months to three years, and short-term consultants on assignments varying in length from a few weeks to a year.

It is anticipated that during a ten-year period each development adviser will spend approximately seven years abroad and three years at Cambridge. While at Cambridge he may write, carry on research, teach, or prepare case materials for courses in development economics, depending upon arrangements worked out before his return to the United States. It is expected that the costs of the operation will be paid from contracts financed by the U.S. Agency for International Development (AID), private foundations, and other assistance agencies. A reserve fund was established at the outset to take care of contingencies and protect the University against loss in the event it should be decided to discontinue operations before reserves can be built up from other sources sufficient to absorb the costs of liquidation.

Let me describe another kind of organization which appears to offer real possibilities for helping to solve the manpower problem and improve the quality of U.S. technical assistance overseas. In 1962, ten U.S. institutions formed a consortium to assist India, under an AID contract, in developing a high-level training and research institution in the field of science and engineering at Kanpur.[1] The consortium arrangement would appear to have a number of advantages. First, it provides a relatively large manpower pool from which to select personnel for overseas service under a system where responsibility for staffing is shared by several institutions. This spreads the burden and avoids situations in which one institution signs an overseas contract, provides part of the personnel, and then recruits from other institutions to meet its remaining needs, a type of operation sometimes referred to as "raiding." The consortium arrangement also encourages each institution to make its really good people available, since no member of the consortium wants to be judged by its peers on the basis of staff members it would like to discard. The consortium makes it possible to do systematic forward planning to meet staffing requirements, and, with a large pool of competent manpower from which to draw, it should be possible to find project leaders who are

---

[1] The consortium includes the Massachusetts Institute of Technology, the California Institute of Technology, the Carnegie Institute of Technology, the Case Institute of Technology, Princeton University, Purdue University, the Ohio State University, the University of California, the University of Michigan, and Educational Services, Inc.

willing to serve overseas for longer than two years, thus providing much-needed continuity of leadership.

A second consortium, this time of four institutions in the Middle West, is now (late 1963) being formed.[2] The total manpower resources of the four institutions will be available in connection with new and existing overseas contracts, whether negotiated in the name of the consortium or by individual institutions. It is anticipated that up to one hundred additional staff members with professional competence for overseas work will be appointed by the four institutions.

In terms of overseas service, this consortium would appear to have all the advantages of the Kanpur science-engineering consortium previously described, with the additional advantage that it is prepared to operate in a number of fields. Located close together as they are and with experience in working together, this group of universities expects to cooperate in relating knowledge and experience gained overseas to on-campus programs of teaching and research. This could turn out to be a major gain, not only for the four institutions, but for scholarship generally.

I would again stress the importance of providing project leadership in some situations for periods of at least five years, and hope that the consortium arrangement will make it possible to do so. Failing this, I would urge the importance of overlapping assignments and other ways of providing continuity of leadership. Without competent, experienced leadership and reasonable continuity, the effectiveness of an overseas mission frequently falls far below its potential.

In the past, the majority of university overseas contracts have been for the purpose of providing relatively long-term assistance in the development of host-country institutions, and this type of assistance will continue to be needed in many situations. The extent to which management as well as policy and organizational advice has been provided has varied, depending upon the trained manpower resources of the host country and whether a completely new or an already established institution was being assisted. In some cases, the U.S. university has at the outset had to assume a sub-

[2] This group at present includes the University of Wisconsin, Michigan State University, the University of Illinois, and Indiana University.

stantial amount of day-to-day management responsibility as well as responsibility for advice on the selection, training, and development of staff and on the development of teaching and research programs.

As overseas institutions develop, there will be increasing need for services involving little if any operating responsibility or management advice on an over-all institutional basis. Short-term consultants on particular problems will be needed from time to time, or specialized staff to help get new courses under way or new research programs off to a good start. Even now there are a number of institutions in developing countries with competent leadership and good staff who need assistance but not of the kind heretofore provided under most university contracts. They do not need advice on institution-wide organization and management, nor do they want to be dependent upon a single U.S. university for assistance. They know that although a particular U.S. university is strong in some fields, it is less strong in others, and they understandably want the best help they can get. Furthermore, as they develop, they begin to feel, and rightly so, that they have progressed to a point where they ought to be treated as equals by U.S. universities. A sister-university relationship under a U.S.-financed contract inevitably involves something of the big-sister, little-sister relationship. Little sisters do not always find this relationship a congenial one, even in the happiest of families.

Perhaps aid agencies should begin to think in terms of grants to overseas universities to enable them to negotiate with U.S. institutions of their choice for such services as they consider they need. I know of one or two grants to American universities to enable them to provide consulting services in specified fields to a foreign institution at the request of the foreign institution. If staff is required by the foreign institution, this is a separate deal, whether the staff is provided by the consulting institution or from some other source. Such an arrangement permits independent action on the part of the foreign institution that is not usually possible under a university-to-university contract. This degree of independence of action is both justified and desirable as institutions in the developing countries achieve competence and acquire confidence.

DEVELOPMENT OF RESEARCH FACILITIES

Other papers in this symposium deal with the organization of agricultural research in the developing countries. I shall confine my remarks to one or two points of a general nature.

If the shift from a traditional to a science-based agriculture is to get off to a good start, the need is to develop as quickly as possible combinations of improved practices that will produce really significant increases in yields—at least 25 to 50 per cent, more if possible. Unless increases in yields are somewhere in this range, the rate of adoption of improved practices by farmers is likely to be disappointingly slow. I shall have more to say about this later on.

Agricultural production is not a mechanical process, but one of facilitating biological growth under almost infinitely varying conditions. Because it is not feasible to alter significantly many important environmental factors, the kinds and varieties of crops grown and the management practices followed must be adjusted to differences in local environment if good results are to be obtained. Standardized recommendations for wide areas are seldom if ever justified.

Adaptive research and experimentation for the purpose of developing combinations of improved practices suited to a wide range of environmental conditions requires a network of experiment stations and testing facilities as well as research institutions engaged in work of a more fundamental character. This often gives rise to difficult organizational questions in the early years of a country's development. Political considerations sometimes result in the scattering of limited resources, particularly of trained manpower, among too many institutions for effective use. The plant breeder in a particular institution may be good but the soils or plant protection specialist poor or lacking entirely.

The development of improved practices that will produce really significant increases in yields usually requires both good facilities and the services of a highly trained staff, well balanced as between the relevant disciplines. Concentrating a developing country's limited research resources in one or two institutions is not likely to be easy in the face of pressures for an agricultural college and experiment station in each major political subdivision.

Recognizing that the goal of every country of substantial size should be to have a good agricultural college and one or more well staffed experiment stations in each major agricultural region, the question still arises as to what to do in the early years if qualified staff is available for only one or two good institutions. The alternatives are to concentrate the best persons available in one or two centers, and to scatter them among a number of centers where they will inevitably be less effective while additional staff is being trained. From the standpoint of agricultural progress, I would vote for concentration in one or two centers in the country's best agricultural region or regions. However, political considerations are likely to force a compromise, and the best that can usually be done is to avoid excessive scatteration of resources until such time as well trained manpower is available to staff all the institutions the country needs.

What can outside assistance agencies do, if anything, about this kind of problem? I suggest two possibilities. First, they can concentrate their efforts in the first instance on helping to develop in each country at least one really good institution whose staff is able to carry on sound research and turn out well trained graduates and postgraduates to staff other institutions and organizations. If enough resources are available to develop more than one such institution, well and good. But it seems to me that, given limited resources, it is better at the outset to concentrate on one or two institutions that give promise of being able to make real contributions to agricultural development within a reasonable period of time than to scatter resources among a large number of institutions, no one of which is likely to amount to much for years to come. The early history of The Rockefeller Foundation's work in Latin America and India seems to me strongly to support this view.

A second possibility is to explore further the development possibilities of regional training and research institutions such as the International Rice Research Institute at Los Baños in the Philippines. This institution, established in 1960 by The Rockefeller and Ford Foundations in cooperation with the Republic of the Philippines, is still quite young. However, experience to date strongly suggests that an organization of this kind can perform the following important functions: (1) By bringing together a competent staff on indefinite tenure, well balanced as among the relevant disciplines, and by providing them with the facilities required for high-quality research and experimentation, it is possible to increase materially the speed with which higher-yielding varieties of crops and improved cultural practices are developed. (2) An important contribution can be made toward training professional personnel within the region in which they expect to work: the high-level manpower required to staff agricultural colleges, experiment stations, extension services, and administrative posts in ministries of agriculture. (3) An institution such as the International Rice Research Institute can serve as catalyst and pace setter —an instrument for helping increase the efficiency and effectiveness of other research, training, and extension organizations in the region it serves. Through its library facilities, its germ plasm banks, its regional seminars and conferences at the working level, and its grants for research work of promise, and by other means, it can stimulate and help improve the quality of research within a large region. (4) Such an institution can demonstrate to visiting administrators and other laymen, in a manner that is not otherwise possible, the kind of balanced, sustained attack that is necessary if the foundations are to be laid for steady and reasonably rapid progress in increasing agricultural production. This can be important in countries where administrators and the public generally have little real understanding of what is involved in shifting a traditional agriculture to an agriculture based on the application of modern science and technology.

In my opinion, a limited number of well staffed regional institutions with adequate facilities and freedom of action, at strategic points in the major underdeveloped regions of the world, could materially speed the process of agricultural development in these regions. They could put teams of highly trained, experienced specialists to work on major problems requiring basic or applied research; they could help train the high-level professional manpower needed in the region; and through regional conferences and seminars, provision of library facilities, exchange of plant materials, and other means, they could make it possible for scientists at other institutions in the region greatly to increase their effectiveness. They would, in effect, perform the kind of function that was performed by a half-dozen leading colleges of agriculture in the United States during the latter part of the last century and the first part of this one. Every state in the Union had at least one agricultural college and a system of experiment stations. But a half-dozen leading institutions set the pace.

If regional institutions of the type I have described are to be successful, the following conditions must be met: (1) Whether financed from public or private funds, they must have independence of action and freedom from political interference. (2) They must be assured of adequate financing for a sufficiently long period of time to enable them to carry out their assigned missions. This will usually require fifteen to twenty years, sometimes longer. If the agency or agencies providing the initial financing for a regional institute are not prepared to finance its operation beyond fifteen or twenty years, it is suggested that the institute be located in the first instance in a country that appears likely to have both the desire and the funds to continue it beyond that time as either a regional or a national resource.

DEVELOPMENT OF EFFECTIVE SUPPLY LINES AND OF STORAGE, TRANSPORTATION, AND MARKETING FACILITIES

Even if farmers are convinced that use of improved seeds, commercial fertilizers, pesticides, and other recommended practices will pay, and are willing to borrow if necessary to buy them, both production supplies and credit must be readily available if improved practices are to be adopted by substantial numbers of producers. Lack of suitable credit at reasonable cost and lack of production supplies of the kinds needed, when and where needed, is a major deterrent to increased production in many developing countries.

This is a problem that needs more attention from foreign assistance agencies. In all too many instances it has been neglected entirely or only a part of the problem has been tackled. Assistance is given in financing a fertilizer plant but nobody worries about how the fertilizer is to be distributed to thousands of villages, some of them far from a railroad or hard-surfaced highway. A great deal of time and effort goes into the development of an improved variety of wheat, corn, or rice, but the system for multiplying and handling seed stocks is often such that the farmer who pays for improved seed does not get what he pays for, but a mixture of varieties instead. This neither increases production materially nor encourages farmers to adopt new practices.

In at least one country, village cooperatives currently have a monopoly of fertilizer distribution. Many of them are too small to be efficient distributors of farm supplies, others are faction-ridden, and still others are poorly managed. Whatever one may think of cooperative organization as a way of life or a way of doing business, giving cooperatives a monopoly has not so far proved a good way to get fertilizer distributed to farmers in this particular country.

Production credit in developing countries is often available only through local moneylenders at high cost or through government or government-sponsored agencies on the basis of predetermined amounts per acre for different crops, instead of being based on an analysis of the farmer's ability to produce and repay his loan. Tenants are often unable to borrow unless the landlord signs the note, and landlords, for a variety of reasons, are frequently reluctant to sign.

Lack of farm-to-market roads and transportation facilities often has an important bearing on cropping patterns. In a village recently visited in East Pakistan, a new road that a bullock cart or small truck can travel has resulted in a substantial increase in the acreage of potatoes grown during the winter months. This shift represents an important increase in the yearly production per acre of food crops.

Loss of grain in storage from insects, rodents, and moisture runs 10 per cent or more in some countries. This is serious if population is pressing heavily upon available food supplies.

What can be done? For one thing, assistance agencies can give more attention to the problem of developing effective supply lines, sources of agricultural credit, and marketing facilities, recognizing that failure to do so may offset to an important degree their efforts in other directions.

There is a wealth of experience and know-how in the United States in producing and distributing supplies and processing and marketing farm products. Large numbers of private business concerns and farmers' cooperatives have been in business for years. Likewise, private lenders, cooperative credit institutions, and government agencies have had a great deal of experience in making loans to farmers and farmers' organizations. So far, we have made too little use of this experience and know-how in our efforts to help developing countries organize for increased agricultural production.

DEVELOPMENT OF INCENTIVES TO ENCOURAGE INCREASED PRODUCTION

I can only point out in passing the importance of the development of incentives in any effort to increase agricultural production in a developing country. Take the problem of risk and uncertainty, for example, as it presents itself to a cultivator with three or four acres of land who is following the farming practices of his forefathers. If he is to obtain substantially increased yields, he must change these practices. He must buy improved seeds, commercial fertilizers, and pesticides, and perhaps make other cash outlays. Whether he uses his own hard-earned savings or borrows to finance the purchase of production supplies and equipment, he faces certain risks—risk of a short crop or even a crop failure, and risk of low prices in case of a large increase in national production. Because his resources are limited, he is not in a position to assume heavy risks. Since failure may sentence him to the life of a landless laborer under circumstances where incomes at the margin are barely sufficient to sustain life, he may well decide to forgo the possibility of increasing his income by adopting new practices in favor of the old ways that, so far at least, have enabled him to eke out an existence and keep his land. More than one country with a large and rapidly growing population pressing heavily on available food supplies has yet to decide that if it wants substantially increased agricultural production, it must provide reasonable security of tenure for its farmers and, by means of price supports and other devices, reduce risk and uncertainty to acceptable levels.

Needless to say, these are difficult and sensitive areas in which to give and accept advice whether in the United States or abroad. They are shot through with conflicting interests and therefore with political considerations. Outside advice clearly cannot be given until it is asked for, and even then the adviser as well as the government which accepts his advice may be the target of sharp criticism. But this fact in no way reduces the importance and urgency of the problem.

DEVELOPING AN EFFECTIVE EXTENSION SERVICE

In most of the developing countries more than half the population is engaged in agriculture. Except in some of the Communist countries, decision making is typically distributed among millions of small operators. Most of them are illiterate and have little capital or little experience outside their home communities. Even where improved practices capable of producing increased yields are available, the job of getting them put to use on millions of small farms is a staggering one.

A dozen papers could be written on the subject of extension work in the developing countries. I shall limit what I have to say to stating six propositions and commenting briefly upon each.

Proposition I. Response to extension work in developing countries is going to be slow at the outset unless relatively simple combinations of improved practices are available, capable of increasing yields by at least 25 to 50 per cent on good soils with good water supplies. Increases of 50 to 100 per cent would be still better.

I suggest that in most circumstances, research workers in developing countries set as their initial target the development of combinations of improved practices that will at least double yields on the better land. This is by no means impossible in many situations. In India and Pakistan, for example, yields of wheat and rice are less than one-third of yields in Japan and one-half of yields in Taiwan.

Experience suggests that after farmers in a developing country become accustomed to buying improved seeds, commercial fertilizers, pesticides, and other production supplies to increase yields, they will respond to smaller increments in yields than those I have just suggested.

Proposition II. Response to extension work will usually be greatest among farmers on the better land, who are owner-operators, and whose farms are of medium to large size by local standards.

This is not to deny the importance of education as it affects the rate at which improved practices are adopted, or the importance of simple as contrasted with complicated packages of practices. I do want to make the point, however, that other factors also affect the rate at which improved practices are adopted. In a district I recently visited in India, only 30 per cent of the tenant farmers have so far adopted a "package" of recommended practices. This is less than half the rate of adoption among owners and part owners. In the best part of the district in terms of soils and water resources, over 80 per cent of the owners have adopted the package, as compared with 36 per cent in the poorest area, where soils are lighter and the water supply less reliable. Only 35 per cent of farmers on owner-operated farms of less than 2.5 acres have adopted the package program, as compared with 50 per cent on farms of 2.5 to 5 acres and 60 per cent on farms of 5 to 20 acres. Beyond 20 acres the rate of adoption dropped off. These are all gross relationships, as are the data on education which Professor Bradfield presents in an earlier paper in this volume. If we are to gain better understanding of the net effect of different variables, including education, further analysis is necessary.

The point I wish to emphasize is that several factors appear to have an important influence on the rate at which improved practices are adopted in developing countries. These should be taken into account in planning extension programs. In view of the "time is running out" consideration that is always present, I would argue that at the outset efforts should be concentrated in those geographic areas and on those farms where promise of quick success is greatest. An important objective at the outset should be to demonstrate, if one can, that *progress is possible*. If this can be demonstrated, time will be gained to work with the "slow adopters."

Agricultural progress never proceeds evenly over a wide geographic area. It certainly has not been even throughout the United States in the past hundred years. Since it is important for an underdeveloped country to get its agriculture moving as fast as it can, and since resources, particularly of trained manpower, are always scarce, the strategy should be to concentrate resources, as far as this is politically possible, on what appear to be the best bets.

Proposition III. Production supplies and credit must be available when needed at reasonable cost in relation to the prices farmers receive for their products, and suitable marketing facilities must be available if farmers in substantial numbers are to adopt recommended practices.

If necessary supplies are not available when they are needed, they obviously cannot be used. If they are priced too high in relation to the prices farmers expect to receive for their products, they will not be used, or they may not be used to the extent that is desirable in terms of national welfare. One country which urgently needs to increase food production is taking a margin on government-produced fertilizer the price of which is now significantly higher in relation to prices farmers receive for wheat and rice than is the case in Japan and the United States. Does this country really want to increase food production or doesn't it?

One thing that always impresses me when I talk with villagers in Asia, Africa, the Middle East, or Latin America is that although few of them can read, they can *all* "figure" in terms of rupees, shillings, or pesos. I am convinced that their basic intelligence and ability correctly to appraise their own economic prospects is greatly underestimated, both at home and abroad.

Proposition IV. Risk of loss, whether from natural causes or from low prices, must be held to tolerable limits if farmers are to respond to the pleas of government to increase production.

Let us keep in mind that in the United States, improved practices have been tested by farmers' experience as well as experimentally; that insurance is available to cover certain kinds of risks; and that for thirty years we have had price supports that have taken much of the price risk out of farming for large numbers of U.S. producers. Also keep in mind that the net worth of the typical U.S. farmer is many times greater than that of the typical Asian, African, or Latin American smallholder. Illiterate farmers respond to considerations of both price and risk as do American farmers.

Proposition V. I am of the opinion that in some developing countries too great emphasis has so far been placed on extension organization and extension teaching methods and too little on subject matter. This is like giving a prospective teacher a dozen courses in methods without checking to find out whether he knows the subject matter he is supposed to teach. Both subject matter and methods are, of course, important.

I think one of the important missing links in the extension services of many developing countries is the person we call the subject-matter specialist. He is the man with an advanced degree who makes it his business to know both the scientific and the applied side of his particular field. He shuttles back and forth between research workers and extension workers, carrying research results to the extension workers and problems back to the research workers. In too many developing countries there is not a sufficiently close working relation between research and extension. When the research worker holds an advanced degree, not to mention a white-collar job, and the extension worker has a high-school education or less plus a thin veneer of special training, the gap between the two services is often hopelessly wide. The subject-matter specialist as we know him can help bridge this gap.

While on the subject of training, let me add that when farmers in developing countries really begin to adopt improved practices, many of the present extension workers are going to find themselves beyond their depth. Usually without first-hand farming experience and with something less than a high-school education plus a two-or three-year training course that often is not very good, they simply are not in a position to answer the difficult questions that immediately arise when farmers begin to shift from a traditional to a science-based agriculture. The fact that a farmer cannot read does not mean he cannot think and ask tough questions. If the person to whom they are addressed cannot answer them, or worse still gives a few wrong answers, and if, in addition, he happens to be young and without farming experience, he is likely to be quickly charged off.

If, as is usually the case, it is necessary at the outset in a developing country to use persons with limited training and experience as extension workers, it is imperative that they be closely backstopped by persons with greater training and experience. Otherwise farmers will quickly lose confidence in the whole operation.

Proposition VI. In most developing countries, extension work is a responsibility of ministries of agriculture rather than of agricultural colleges. This also applies to research in many cases. We in the United States, accustomed to the trinity of teaching, research, and extension in our land-grant colleges, are sometimes inclined to question the workability of any other system.

Even if one feels, as I do, that our system has much to commend it in our own setting, it does not follow that the wise course is to suggest that the existing system in another country be junked with a view to introducing a brand-new American model. Bureaucratic organizations in developing countries are likely to be as difficult to liquidate as they are at home. In any case, I would raise the question whether it may not be better in most cases to try to increase the effectiveness of existing organizations than to try to kill them off and start anew. This is not because I believe in bureaucratic peace at any price, but because I am not sure the greatest progress is always made by frontal attack on systems that happen to be different from our own. It is quite possible for types of organization other than our own to function effectively.

Conclusion

In closing let me emphasize a point we are all in the process of learning the hard way. Economic, social, and political development, because it involves changes in people and their organizational arrangements for working together, is a long, slow process better measured in decades and generations than in years. This is true in Keokuk and Kalamazoo as well as in Kano and Karachi.

Agricultural progress in the developing countries is going to be slow. Much research and experimentation remains to be done to develop improved combinations of practices suitable for use in a wide variety of local environments. Farmers have to be convinced that recommended practices can be depended upon to produce increased yields and that it is to their advantage to adopt them. Farm supply lines have to be opened, marketing facilities created or perfected, and national economic policies adjusted to realities if farmers are to respond to the need for increased production.

But having emphasized some of the difficulties, I want to close on a note of optimism. Progress *is* being made although much of it is not yet visible for all to see. I recently visited two agricultural areas in India and one in East Pakistan. Improved practices are being adopted in these areas by owner-operators on good land whose holdings are large enough so that the increase in output, and therefore in income, has meaning. Increases in production in these districts are not yet sufficient to have a significant effect on state or national totals. *But despite handicaps, a start has been made.*

We and our friends in the developing countries are also beginning to recognize and gain insights into some of the organizational problems and policy questions with which they are going to have to deal if agricultural production is to be increased significantly. Again, progress is not always highly visible, but it is there if one looks for it.

This is not the time to get discouraged, much less to give up. It is now clear that most of us expected too much too soon. Perhaps we are now in danger of becoming too pessimistic.

I doubt whether progress is going to be spectacular during the next decade. But if we continue to work at the job in the future as we have in the past, the world's food supply can be greatly increased. Whether the increase will be ultimately offset by increases in population remains, of course, to be seen.

SUMMARY

If the less developed countries are substantially to increase agricultural production, traditional agriculture must give way to an agriculture based on the application of modern science and technology. This requires the services of large numbers of persons trained in agriculture to staff agricultural colleges and experiment stations, extension services, government departments, and industries and businesses producing and distributing agricultural supplies and marketing agricultural products. Most of the personnel required must be trained at home.

The development of an effective educational and research institution in a newly developing country usually requires ten to fifteen years or longer. Few U.S. universities are organized to help effectively with this kind of job. It is particularly important that the *leaders* of assistance missions engaged in long-term institution-building activities be available to serve for, say, a minimum of five years. Several U.S. universities are engaged in promising experiments with consortia and other new forms of organization to provide overseas services.

There is need for a great deal of agricultural research and experimentation in the developing countries to develop improved crop varieties and cultural practices suited to a wide variety of local conditions. To avoid unwise scattering of limited resources, foreign assistance agencies should encourage the development of at least one or two well staffed institutions in each country, capable of turning out well trained graduates and doing competent research. High-level regional training and research institutions, independently staffed and managed, can make major contributions toward improving the quality of training and research in a whole region.

Major factors limiting production in many developing countries are: failure to develop an effective system for producing and distributing improved seeds, fertilizers, pesticides, and other production supplies; and lack of suitable credit facilities for agriculture. Price-cost relations in agriculture and land tenure arrangements are of basic importance in their bearing on the willingness of farmers to make investments for the purpose of increasing production.

Development of an effective agricultural extension service is of major importance to a developing country, but must be based on adequate research and experimentation.

If a developing country wishes substantially to increase production by shifting from a traditional to a modern agriculture, it must be prepared to make large investments, public and private, in education, research, extension, transportation, storage, processing plants, marketing facilities, and credit facilities. Heavy investment may also be necessary as part of a program of land reform.

Outside assistance, to be most effective, must be organized on a long-term basis and should be continued at or near the established level long enough to enable the developing country to "take off" on its own.

New Patterns of Agricultural Research and Education in India

ALBERT H. MOSEMAN

Director for Agricultural Sciences, The Rockefeller Foundation, New York

IN A RECENT REVIEW of progress in American agriculture, Dr. Byron T. Shaw (1963), administrator of the United States Department of Agriculture's Agricultural Research Service, pointed out that the crop and livestock output of U.S. farms today is 60 per cent higher than it was in 1939. Farmers in 1963 used 8 per cent less cropland and less than half as many man-hours of farm labor.

In 1939 the corn crop from 88 million acres totaled 2.6 billion bushels. In 1963 the harvest of more than 4 billion bushels will come from about 61 million acres—75 per cent more corn from 27 million fewer acres. The national average yield for the United States in 1963 is estimated at 67.3 bushels per acre.

The 1939 wheat crop of 741 million bushels required 53 million acres. In 1963 the 1.1 billion bushels were harvested from 45.3 million acres.

The steady increase in yield per acre or output per man-hour in crop and livestock production continues to demonstrate the effective application of science and technology in U.S. agriculture. We are reaping the benefits of research in many disciplines that have converged to boost production spectacularly during the past two decades.

Within these past two decades we have engaged in many and varied efforts to assist war-torn and newly independent nations to advance their economies. Some of these ventures have been fruitful, but on balance we have not reaped the broad benefits we might have anticipated. Mexico has achieved self-sufficiency in wheat and corn production during the past twenty years. Mexico, Taiwan,

Greece, Israel, and a few other countries can point to outstanding growth rates in agriculture and in their general economy that averaged 5 per cent or more annually for more than a decade. There is yet much uncertainty, however, whether the progress achieved with outside resources in some countries will be maintained when the external assistance is withdrawn.

AGRICULTURE AND ECONOMIC DEVELOPMENT

There is a continuing, and perhaps inevitable, imbalance in most developing countries with respect to agricultural versus industrial growth. As stated by Rostow (1963), agriculture has three essential roles to play in promoting growth:

First, agriculture must supply the food required by rapidly expanding urban populations in the developing countries. If the demand is not met, there may be hunger—even starvation; or food must be acquired from abroad, which depletes the foreign exchange needed to import industrial equipment and raw materials.

Second, agricultural expansion is required as working capital for non-agricultural development—to generate raw materials for industry, to earn foreign exchange, and to free labor from agriculture and make it available for industrial construction and operation.

Third, a rise in agricultural incomes stimulates other aspects of development. It provides the capital accumulation needed for further growth, through savings required for investment or as a critically important source of increased tax revenues. It also provides expanded markets for industry—chemical fertilizers, agricultural equipment and manufactured consumers' goods.

Although advances in agriculture are basic to accelerated economic progress, Rostow points out: "The brutal fact is, however, that the diffusion of modern methods in rural life is going too slowly for the good of the developing countries. It may be useful for those concerned to take stock of what we have learned from experiments in various parts of the world and to consider explicitly how the diffusion process, now rather laborious and expensive, can be broadened and accelerated."

AGRICULTURAL PROGRESS IN THE UNITED STATES

The review of our own agricultural development will disclose that until the beginning of World War II the added needs for agricultural products were met largely by cropping new lands. Acre yields remained nearly constant through the 1930's, when we still benefited from the millions of added acres that were available for food production as mechanization released the lands previously used to grow feed for horses and mules. During the period beginning in the 1920's, however, the added emphasis on research, especially by the USDA and the land-grant colleges, laid the groundwork for the superabundance of today.

More productive plants and animals became available from research in genetics, breeding, and nutrition. Crop plants were bred for improved adaptation, with disease resistance and higher consumer quality. More effective controls were evolved for pests and weeds. Soil and water management practices were perfected. Fertilizers were used with greater precision. Farm machines were designed to increase efficiency and timeliness of many operations, from soil preparation through harvesting.

These and other developments came from the many scientific disciplines that were focused effectively on problems that inhibit agricultural production. The growth of our agricultural output has come from the combined application of new knowledge and new materials. This is a complicated process, and, as we consider the task of agricultural development in new nations, we might recall that materials and methods for hybrid corn production were not "extended" directly from Iowa to North Carolina without substantial research and testing. As Dr. F. F. Hill has stated on occasion, "It has taken us some time to find out that what works in Keokuk will not always work in Karachi."

We are realizing more and more that it is not possible to "extend" U.S. materials and methods abroad, and we should be increasingly aware of the need to approach agricultural development in an organized manner, through institutions that will foster research and testing and the related aspects of education, including the transfer of innovations into practice.

THE INSTITUTIONAL BASE FOR AGRICULTURE IN THE
UNITED STATES

There are many organizations that serve our domestic agriculture. They are closely interdependent, and could not be reestablished in their total form abroad, even if it were deemed desirable to do so. We can, however, benefit from some analysis of our major research and educational institutions and select a few of the principles that might have utility in advancing agriculture elsewhere.

My subject is "New Patterns of Agricultural Research and Education in India." The patterns to which I shall refer have evolved from the application of experience drawn from the land-grant colleges and from the USDA and their programs of research, education, and extension. It may be helpful to assess a few of the relevant features of these U.S. institutions as a backdrop to the Indian scene.

The Land-Grant Colleges

There has been much enthusiasm for the idea of transplanting the U.S. land-grant college into rural areas abroad. This has considerable merit if we think in terms of the *functions* of education, research, and extension, rather than the precise form of organization, and also if we appreciate the scope and limitations of such institutions.

The land-grant system was designed to furnish greater educational opportunity for the working and industrial classes, and because of the highly agrarian orientation in the United States in 1862, strong emphasis was placed initially on agriculture. The agricultural sciences evolved largely through a broadening of the scope of understanding and interest of the traditional economic botanist, zoologist, and other narrowly defined academic disciplines, as the college staff endeavored to understand and combat the multitude of problems in rural areas. In analyzing the unique contribution of the land-grant colleges to experimental science it has long been recognized that professors were hired at these institutions to teach agriculture before the science of agriculture had been developed. It was necessary, therefore, for students and their

President Radhakrishnan addresses the first convocation of the Uttar Pradesh Agricultural University at Pantnagar. In the background is the main University building. (*Photo by courtesy of USIS, India*)

One of the promising experimental sorghum hybrids selected in the cooperative research program

Dwarf wheats from the Mexican Agricultural Program promise to increase yields of this crop substantially in India.

Students of the Uttar Pradesh Agricultural University take a soil sample. The University is the first of several higher educational institutions patterned on American land-grant colleges which have been established in India. (*Photo by courtesy of USIS, India*)

professors to work with the materials at hand and start experimenting with them.

The educational programs of the land-grant colleges were designed to expose students to knowledge in a number of disciplines or areas of interest, and this created a large body of scientists and technicians capable of understanding many aspects of practical problems. Such students retained a certain affinity for the land and they were challenged by problems in the field. The movement of these people into the extension service, and the constant interchange with their college colleagues concerned with research and education, ensured a continuous flow of science and technology into practice. Equally important has been the attention to education at all levels, from Ph.D. training to farm operators' short courses—an important factor in the acceptance of innovations.

In evaluating the potential of the land-grant college as an institution for advancement of agriculture in developing nations, we should keep in mind the fact that, as stated by Dr. W. Robert Parks (1963), "the land-grant system is a nation-wide system of higher education. The Morrill Act of 1862 put into effect this brave new radical idea of a whole nation-wide system of higher education in one fell swoop." Later, the Hatch Act of 1887 gave birth to the nation-wide chain of state-run experiment stations, and the Smith-Lever Act of 1914 laid the groundwork for a nation-wide group of state extension services. The land-grant colleges were designed to serve essentially a state-wide *geographic* area in the *functional* areas of agricultural education, research, and extension.

When we recall that agricultural progress in the United States benefited from 68 land-grant institutions, we may assess the effectiveness—or the limitations—of a single college or university in an advancing nation. If only one such institution is developed, it may well serve as a pattern, or establish a level of excellence, but its impact in creating change, on a national level, will probably be minimal.

The United States Department of Agriculture

All people of a nation are concerned about the adequacy of supplies of food, fiber, and other products of agriculture. A national organization to foster progress in agriculture is, therefore, essential. The USDA has pioneered in many fields, from the early introduction of new plant and animal germ plasm, and the creation of field stations and laboratories for study of agriculture under dry-land conditions and under irrigation as new lands came under cultivation, to the current provision of a multitude of services to farmers, organizations related to agriculture, and consumers.

The nature of the research and extension activities of the land-grant or "people's colleges," reaching into the counties and interacting with farm people, is a source of strength in their service to agricultural development. Though this intensive "local orientation" provides the colleges with some insulation from national social and political forces, they are subject to many state and local pressures which tend to accentuate the accumulation of new materials or knowledge in a fractured or fragmented pattern in the separate institutions. The USDA has functioned most effectively as a coordinating partner in bringing together these independent contributions of many state experiment station scientists.

Dr. H. K. Hayes (1963), professor emeritus of the Division of Agronomy and Plant Genetics of the University of Minnesota, has stated that the real impetus for the practical development of hybrid corn in the United States came from the establishment, in 1925, of the cooperative program of the corn belt state experiment stations and the USDA under the Purnell Act. This program, under the coordinating leadership of Dr. F. D. Richey of the USDA, fostered the exchange of materials and ideas, and the planning of uniform experiments that furnished data from many locations in a given year. This pattern of cooperation was extended subsequently to research for improvement of most other major crops and livestock in the United States and permitted simultaneous attention to problems of local, regional, and national concern. Moreover, it minimized duplication, so that a maximum return was received from public investments in the state and federal research institutions.

Shaw (1963), in discussing the working relations of the Department and the state agricultural experiment stations, stated, "We cooperate formally on more than half of our research, and informally on most of the rest. I am convinced that this Federal-State cooperative system, which has stimulated the development of strong agricultural research institutions in each state, is largely responsible for the outstanding progress that has been made in agricultural research during the last 70 years."

Another point that should not be overlooked is that the USDA serves as the prime target for requests from groups with special interests in some aspect of the agricultural industry, and although these may bring mixed blessings, they do tend to ensure constant research attention to the many practical problems that inhibit agricultural progress.

As we direct our efforts to assist with agricultural development in advancing nations, we must do a better job of isolating the pertinent features of our own science and technology which today enable about 7 per cent of our population to feed 192 million people, with an excess for export, on the smallest acreage in 50 years (USDA, 1963). The achievement of such abundance through advances in conventional crop and livestock production gives hope for similar accomplishment abroad if we select appropriate, effective tools for the task.

INDIA—GENERAL

Chester Bowles (1963), who returned in April 1963 to the post of United States Ambassador to India, in which he served from 1951 to 1953, suggests:

It is imperative that Americans see the whole of India, with all its complexities, frustrations and promise; that, above all, we understand what its leaders and people are seeking to do and the nature of their successes and failures.

The most casual glance at the map and a cursory understanding of political realities underscore the importance of a viable India—with its population greater than Latin America and Africa combined, a rich and deeply rooted culture, a growing economic potential and a strong democratic commitment. India's success or failure will have a major impact on tomorrow's world.

India's population of 450 million is increasing by about 10 mil-

lion annually. Three-fourths of her people are illiterate, and life
expectancy of 40 years is well below the European and U.S. level
of 70 years. The Central Government must serve a population with
12 major languages, and many minor ones, in 16 states. India's
social-political complex is akin to what might be encountered if
the countries of Europe, excluding Russia, with a total population
slightly less than India's, were to be united under a single government.

India inherited a government that was concerned more with
the maintenance of order than with economic development, or
with advances in levels of living for the Indian people. Significant
progress has been made to date in reducing the number of states
from more than 500 to today's 16; in raising literacy from 10 per
cent to 25 per cent, and bringing 70 per cent of Indian school-age
children under 12 into school; in increasing life expectancy from
27 years to over 40; in increasing, since 1953, electric power output fourfold, steel production threefold, and over-all industrial
production by 100 per cent.

Indian Agriculture

India's 300 million acres of arable land must produce food for
450 million people and feed for 200 million cattle. Crop yields
are among the world's lowest, with rough rice or paddy yields of
1350 pounds per acre as compared with Japan's 4330 pounds
(Ewell, 1963). Yields of wheat, barley, millet, and other crops are
also about one-third of those in Japan. The potential for increased
agricultural production is large, through breeding and increased
use of improved crop varieties, double cropping and better tillage
practices, more precise use of fertilizers and pest control practices,
and more effective water use. India currently applies only 1 pound
of nitrogen per acre of agricultural land, in contrast with 100
pounds in Japan, 20 to 100 pounds in western European countries,
13 pounds in the United States, and 3 pounds in the U.S.S.R. India
added 20 million acres during the past decade to what was already
the largest irrigated area in the world (51.5 million acres in 1950),
and plans to add 18 million acres more, an area greater than
Michigan, during the present Five-Year Plan, which ends in 1966.

India's goal of increasing output of food grains by about 6 per cent annually during this Five-Year Plan period—to over 100 million tons by 1966—will be achieved, however, only if the development and application of improved technology is accelerated.

INDIAN AGRICULTURAL INSTITUTIONS, 1947

Agricultural research and education in India at, and immediately following, Independence was not effective in advancing agricultural production. The major support for research was through the Agricultural Research Institute at New Delhi, the Veterinary Research Institute at Izatnagar, and the smaller National or Central Research Institutes or Stations concerned with selected crops, including rice, potatoes, vegetables, and sugar cane, and with forestry, fisheries, and dairy production.

The Central Commodity Committees for cotton, sugar cane, tobacco, oilseeds, jute, and other crops were empowered to use revenues from a special tax or cess on these products to support research and services.

The Indian Council of Agricultural Research financed selected projects and also served as the clearinghouse and coordinating agency for agricultural research in the country.

In 1919 the states were given primary responsibility for agriculture, a responsibility which was retained under the present Indian constitution. The states, however, lacked the financial resources to mount adequate research programs.

The colleges of agriculture functioned for the most part in training men for the government service. According to Dr. F. W. Parker (1958), in 1947 there were 27 agricultural and veterinary colleges with 996 students enrolled. Most of the agricultural colleges, except three private ones, and all the veterinary colleges were administered by the state departments of agriculture or animal husbandry. They were primarily teaching institutions. The principal of the college had no responsibility for research and the colleges neither engaged in nor taught extension. Teaching was from dictated lecture notes, with the syllabus for each subject fixed by the university with which the college was affiliated. All students took the same course, with no electives. There were few examinations during the year, and the student was evaluated by a board of external examiners at the end of the year. The administrative rigidity imposed by the affiliation with universities, whose leaders had little appreciation of the needs of agriculture, rendered the colleges almost entirely ineffective. As Parker (1958) pointed out, "Their 'ivory tower' situation was exemplified by the fact that, when the Government of India launched its ambitious community development program [in 1952], these colleges were not involved in the program in any way."

INTENSIVE REVIEWS OF INDIAN AGRICULTURAL RESEARCH AND EDUCATION

Indian leaders recognized, almost from the day of Independence, that changes were needed in their agricultural educational system. In 1948 the University Education Commission was appointed, with Dr. S. Radhakrishnan, now the distinguished President of India, as its chairman. Dr. John J. Tigert, former president of the University of Florida, and Mr. Arthur E. Morgan, former chairman of the Board, Tennessee Valley Authority, were named to the Commission, furnishing immediate United States cooperation. The Commission's report recognized the inadequacy of agricultural education under the existing pattern of agricultural colleges in affiliating universities, and strongly recommended the establishment of "rural universities," with many of the characteristics and functions of U.S. land-grant colleges.

Though the University Education Commission pointed up the need for change in agricultural education, the implementation of such change was initiated primarily by the U.S. Technical Cooperation Mission to India, established in 1952 (now U.S. Agency for International Development). Early attention was given to assisting the Indian agricultural and veterinary colleges and research institutes, and in March 1954 an agreement was reached to establish a Joint Indo-American Team on Agricultural Research and Education. The Team was directed to "make a comparative study of the organization, functions and working of Indian and American agricultural and research institutions and agricultural colleges and make recommendations . . . to remove some of the critical deficiencies in the existing facilities for agricultural research and education in India" (USDA, 1963). It was also to "suggest methods for coordinating the work of such institutions in India functioning under the Center, the States and the Universities."

The five Indian members of the Team spent ten weeks in the United States, early in 1955, studying research and education, including the cooperative research of the land-grant colleges and the USDA. The three Americans then spent nearly three months in India reviewing the work of the colleges of agriculture, the Central Research Institutes, and other organizations concerned with agricultural research and education. The Team report of September 1955 (ICAR, 1955) contained 118 specific recommendations, which, together with the University Education Commission report, served to guide many of the subsequent actions.

A second Indo-American Team, in 1959, again reviewed the status of agricultural research and education in the country and made further proposals for its improvement.

New Patterns in Agricultural Education

In the period July to October 1955, simultaneously with the review of the first Joint Indo-American Team, two-man survey teams from the Universities of Illinois, Missouri, and Tennessee, Ohio State University, and Kansas State College visited India for periods of four to six weeks to study possible cooperative efforts to improve education and research programs in five different regions of India. Subsequently contracts were signed with the U.S. Technical Cooperation Mission providing for assistance from Ohio State University to the states in northwestern India, the University of Illinois to north central India, the University of Missouri to northeastern India, the University of Tennessee to southern India, and Kansas State College to south central and southwestern India.

In 1956 the Government of India and The Rockefeller Foundation entered into a cooperative agreement which provided for Foundation assistance in the development of a postgraduate school at the Indian Agricultural Research Institute and also in directing research to improve production of certain food grains, with initial emphasis on corn, sorghums, and millets. The Foundation's field director, Dr. Ralph W. Cummings, brought to the position a background of land-grant college experience in coordinating attention to education, research, and extension. As former director of the North Carolina Agricultural Experiment Station system he also had abundant experience in cooperative research with the USDA in crop improvement, soil management, agricultural engineering, and other fields.

THE POST GRADUATE SCHOOL OF THE INDIAN AGRICULTURAL RESEARCH INSTITUTE

In implementing the cooperative effort to establish the Post Graduate School at the Indian Agricultural Research Institute, Dr. Cummings served an initial period as dean of the School and furnished guidance, through a council composed of scientific personnel of the Institute, in developing a pattern of teaching, examination schedules, and provision for combinations of courses to ensure greater breadth of training than was previously available through the affiliating universities in India. These modifications were thoroughly reviewed and considered by the Indian professors of the College and were activated only after agreement by the council. The resulting teaching program embodied many of the features of graduate-level education in our land-grant universities. The Post Graduate School was given independent degree-granting authority by the Indian University Grants Commission on July 8, 1958, and was inaugurated in October of that year.

More than 400 students are now enrolled in the Post Graduate School, of whom about 45 per cent are studying for the Ph.D. degree and the others for the M.Sc. A total of 99 Ph.D. degrees and 322 M.Sc. degrees have been granted through the most recent convocation, held on December 20, 1963.

Following the successful establishment of the Post Graduate School, the Government of India appointed a committee, in 1961, to advise the state governments in the establishment of agricultural universities. In naming this committee it was pointed out that "the urgency of bringing about a rapid increase in food production in this country necessitates a re-examination of the existing patterns with the aim of bringing about the greatest possible efficiency and effectiveness of the organizations serving agriculture. It is apparent that there is a need for establishing much closer relationships between research, teaching and extension programs which is not possible under the existing arrangements. It is with these aims in view that the concept of the Agricultural University has been developed" (ICAR, 1962).

In developing the pattern of the agricultural university the following features were recognized, to distinguish the proposed agricultural university from the traditional university (AID, 1962).

(1) It recognizes a responsibility and responsiveness to the needs of cultivators in contrast with being only a seat of learning and scholarship, and assumes a responsibility for working towards the economic development and improvement of the standard of living of the people of the state.

(2) In addition to resident teaching for degree candidates, the staff also have responsibility for applied as well as fundamental research in agriculture. Such research must go beyond the laboratory and into the fields and homes, and with the livestock, under varying conditions found in different parts of the State.

(3) The chief medium through which the cultivators are to derive the benefits of the training programmes and of the research work under the agricultural university, is the extension limb of the university, which should be fully integrated with teaching and research organizations so that a smooth and effective flow of the results of research and of the training programmes to the cultivators be possible and the problems of the cultivators may similarly be transmitted back to the teaching and training centers for being tackled promptly and effectively.

(4) The territory of the university with respect to the agricultural and related sciences should include the entire state, in keeping with the above principles and responsibilities.

(5) The curricula and the training programmes should be modelled in a manner as to be in keeping with the needs of the state on the one hand and of the aptitudes and needs of the individual students or trainees on the other. This must involve the formulation of a flexible curriculum with suitable provisions for courses of instruction in a wide field and the appointment of teachers who have specialized in their respective disciplines.

It is the stated policy of the Government of India that an autonomous agricultural university be developed in each state. Dr.

Cummings was asked to chair the Agricultural University Committee, and the U.S. AID Mission has a representative on the Committee. AID support, as well as Government of India support, to the new agricultural universities has been based on the recommendations of this committee (AID, 1962).

THE UTTAR PRADESH AGRICULTURAL UNIVERSITY

Substantial progress has been made in developing two of the agricultural universities. The first was established in 1960 in the state of Uttar Pradesh, in north central India, on the 16,000-acre Tarai State Farm, with financial support from AID and with technical guidance from the University of Illinois. This Agricultural University has pioneered on the academic side, and it now has Colleges of Agriculture, Veterinary and Animal Science, and Agricultural Engineering, and a School of Basic Science and Humanities. At its first convocation, on November 17, 1963, 99 students were graduated with the B.S. degree in agriculture and animal husbandry, having completed the three-year course after intermediate college. The first students in the veterinary course, which requires four years, will be graduated in June 1964. Postgraduate work in the agricultural sciences was initiated in July 1963 with approximately 60 candidates for the M.Sc. degree.

Excellent progress has been made in developing a 500-acre experiment station farm as a part of the campus. Approximately 100 acres are set aside for student practice, 5-acre tracts being assigned to groups of 8 to 10 students in their senior year. The students are responsible for planning the cropping practices. They conduct all the work, pay for the use of the implements, fertilizer, insecticides, seed, and so on, and are responsible for harvesting and marketing the crop.

The cooperative corn improvement project is the most significant research activity at the experiment station, but other projects are under way in the various departments. The University is also developing its extension program, with an extension director and a small group of extension specialists furnishing leadership for technical subject-matter areas in three extension blocks in the state. As yet, the state government has not transferred to the University responsibility for the regular research or extension programs carried by the state Department of Agriculture.

THE PUNJAB AGRICULTURAL UNIVERSITY

The Agricultural University for the Punjab, which includes the Colleges of Agriculture at Ludhiana and Hissar and the College of Animal and Veterinary Science at Hissar, was formally established in October 1962. Ohio State University is furnishing the technical guidance for this Agricultural University, under AID financing.

Colleges of Basic Science and Humanities, Agricultural Engineering, and Home Science will be located at Ludhiana; and a College of Basic Science and Humanities will be added to the Agricultural and the Veterinary Science Colleges at Hissar. Each of the two campuses has a separate dean, but there is one director of research and one director of extension for the entire University. At the department level each subject-matter discipline will have a department head in residence at one campus and an associate department head at the second campus.

The Agricultural University Center at Ludhiana has a farm and campus of approximately 1200 acres, and considerable progress has been made in developing a first-class research station. The 2000-acre tract at Hissar also is being improved for experimental work.

All the agricultural research programs and stations of the state have been transferred to the direction of the University. The research is being consolidated at a reduced number of well equipped and adequately staffed regional centers.

An extension director has been appointed, and subject-matter specialists are provided for in the various departments in the College of Agriculture. In addition, the University will have, initially, four subject-matter specialists in each of the districts, and they expect eventually to extend such specialist help into the various blocks.

Postgraduate work has been initiated, with the trimester system of course work and instruction. It is expected that the trimester system and internal examinations will be introduced at the undergraduate level in another year.

The Agricultural University of the Punjab is developing as one
of the really effective patterns or pace setters among the group of
emerging agricultural institutions in India. It reflects the able and
effective assistance that has been furnished by Ohio State University personnel since 1956. The strong leadership of Vice-Chancellor P. N. Thapar, formerly Secretary to the Government of India,
Ministry of Agriculture, is another most important element in the
future impact of this institution.

OTHER AGRICULTURAL UNIVERSITIES

Legislation has been enacted for the establishment of agricultural universities by the governments of Orissa, Rajasthan, West
Bengal, Mysore, Madhya Pradesh, and Andhra Pradesh. Discus-
sions of legislation and tentative plans also are under way in other
states.

The decision to follow the pattern of developing agricultural
universities as "one of the most effective and enduring institutions
for creating the human resources needed for the national development of India" (AID, 1962) is based on continuous study by
Indian leaders at all levels, including President S. Radhakrishnan.

In his statement before the Association of Land-Grant Colleges
and Universities in Kansas City on November 13, 1961, Dr. K. A.
P. Stevenson, vice-chancellor of the new agricultural university in
the state of Uttar Pradesh, brought the needs of Indian agricultural
education into focus when he said, "Many underdeveloped countries, including my own, India, have an existing system of university education, but the fact remains that this system does not
meet the needs of our people. We want a more dynamic approach
—something nearer the aspirations of the bulk of our people—
and it is this spirit of service to the community, a spirit introduced
in your country by the Land-Grant college, that we would like
to foster in our country."

The AID Mission, in its report in 1962, stated, "The agricultural
university program and the approach to it through contracts with
U.S. universities is considered by this Division [Agriculture] to be
one of the best approaches to the development of human resources
in the agricultural area. It is an essential part of meeting the critical
skilled manpower problem of India—educated manpower willing

to work on the land with the farmer and dedicated to the service of the farmer" (AID, 1962).

There are still many problems to be resolved in the organization of agricultural universities in the various states and in assigning state-wide responsibility for research, education, and extension to the universities. The Government of India, however, hopes to have an agricultural university in each state by the end of the Fourth Five-Year Plan, in 1971.

Questions have been raised relative to the number of agricultural universities that should be established in India. If we keep in mind the fact that 68 land-grant institutions have supplied much of the leadership for agricultural development in the United States, it does not seem unreasonable for India to plan for at least 15, to serve essentially half the land mass but about the same agricultural acreage, and a population about 2.5 times that of the United States. About 75 per cent of India's population is tied to the land, concerned with agricultural production under widely diverse environments and cropping patterns. The Agricultural University of Uttar Pradesh faces a formidable challenge, for example, in serving that state's population of nearly 77 million, a total that is more than double the U.S. population of about 35 million in 1862, when our nation-wide system of land-grant colleges was established.

It will be necessary for India to furnish the major financing and resources for the agricultural universities, but some outside support will be essential for the development of a sufficient number of these institutions to demonstrate the effectiveness of the coordination of effort between them and with the Central Government in research, education, and extension to project the pattern or image needed to guide the development of a nation-wide institutional system.

New Patterns in Agricultural Research

In reviewing the modifications in Indian agricultural research I should like to draw primarily upon the cooperative program in crop improvement initiated in 1956, when the agreement was signed by The Rockefeller Foundation and the Ministry of Agriculture of the Government of India.

In the implementation of this cooperative effort it was recognized from the beginning that in addition to the research to improve yields and production of the specific crops, and training of indigenous personnel, a concerted effort should be made to establish a pattern of effective cooperation between the Central Government and state government organizations to assure maximum use of India's research resources.

The cooperative corn improvement scheme is supported primarily by the Indian Council of Agricultural Research, with supplemental support from the ministries of agriculture of the central and state governments. In order to achieve maximum understanding among local personnel and to expedite eventual transfer of leadership responsibility, the work is conducted within the existing organizations, primarily the Botany and Agronomy Divisions of the Indian Agricultural Research Institute, the state directorates of agriculture, and the new agricultural universities. A Foundation staff member is designated as the coordinating leader of the project, with an Indian colleague as assistant coordinator. Periodic conferences of the state and Central Government scientists assure mutual understanding in planning and conduct of the research.

A specific effort was made to locate the regional research centers at state institutions which would have responsibility for research and education, and where extension programs might eventually be associated. The possibility of establishing an agricultural university for the state of Uttar Pradesh at the Tarai State Farm was taken into account in locating the regional center for the Gangetic Plain, in January 1957. The corn improvement scheme is now the major research endeavor of the experiment station of the Uttar Pradesh Agricultural University, which was established in 1960. The cooperative research in the Punjab was shifted to Ludhiana when the Punjab Agricultural University was established there. The cooperative corn, sorghum, and millet schemes are similarly tied into the Colleges of Agriculture at Coimbatore and Hyderabad, where it is anticipated that future state agricultural universities will come into being.

The Rockefeller Foundation has intentionally furnished a limited technical staff for guidance of the cooperative corn improvement scheme, in order to encourage maximum participation from Indian scientists in the various disciplines. The initial Foundation corn breeder was joined by a second plant breeder after the first year of operation. Subsequently it has been decided that added staff in entomology and in engineering (to assist in improving experimental fields or stations) and a soil scientist were required to ensure continuing research attention to these related scientific areas. The provision of a small, competent, but continuing staff has made it possible to join forces most effectively with a larger number of participating Indian scientists and also has permitted the efficient use of short-term consultants or appointees who can fit into the main stream of an established program.

In addition to the production, and release for growing, of seven adapted, high-yielding hybrids since 1957, and the transfer of increasing responsibility for coordination of the corn improvement scheme to the Indian counterpart, the most significant contribution of this cooperative project has been through the pattern established for effective and efficient agricultural research. The Government of India is now restudying other agricultural problem areas and has decided that additional research should be patterned after the corn improvement scheme. The Government of India has also asked The Rockefeller Foundation to support a review team to study further the improvement of agricultural research, education, and extension in India, with special emphasis on the coordination of the efforts in these three functions, and on improved coordination of the research activities of the Central Government and the states. In requesting this team, the Government of India suggested that it consist of a scientist to represent the U.S. Department of Agriculture, to furnish understanding of national research programs; an individual experienced in land-grant university functions; an individual qualified in the animal sciences; and a representative of the British Agricultural Research Council. The review team, under the leadership of Dr. M. W. Parker, director of crops research, USDA; Dr. R. L. Lovvorn, director of the North Carolina Experiment Station; Dr. O. B. Ross, head of the Department of Animal Science, University of Illinois; and Dr. E. E. Cheesman of the British Agricultural Research Council, completed an initial six weeks' review on December 15, 1963, and their preliminary report is available for study prior to completion of the review in March 1964.

SUMMARY AND CONCLUSIONS

Government of India leaders were aware, at the time of Independence in 1947, that existing agricultural research and educational programs were ineffective in advancing India's primitive agriculture.

A continuing series of reviews have been conducted jointly by Indian and U.S. scientists, who have studied the Indian institutions and also the U.S. Department of Agriculture and the land-grant colleges, together with U.S. procedures for coordinating research, education, and extension at state and national levels. The first of these studies was conducted by the University Education Commission, established in 1948 under the chairmanship of Dr. S. Radhakrishnan, now President of India.

On the basis of these reviews, Government of India scientists and educators concluded that institutions should be developed that would ensure more intensive focus on the significant factors inhibiting progress in Indian agriculture. The University Education Commission in 1948 recommended that agricultural universities be established, embodying the principles of the U.S. land-grant colleges.

Agricultural universities have been established in the states of Uttar Pradesh and the Punjab, with technical guidance from the University of Illinois and Ohio State University and financing from AID. Legislation to establish agricultural universities has been passed by six additional states and is pending or being studied by other state governments.

In addition to agricultural universities to furnish the institutional base for education, research, and extension at the state level, the need was recognized for improved coordination of effort by the central and state government agencies concerned with science and technology, and with other features of agricultural development.

The cooperative corn improvement scheme supported by The Rockefeller Foundation, the Indian Council of Agricultural Research, and the central and state governments of India has functioned effectively since 1957 and is furnishing a pattern of coordinated effort in agricultural research that is being adopted in other research projects in India.

In the development of the agricultural universities and the coordinated center-state research programs, the general image of U.S. institutions was accepted, but determined efforts were made to apply basic principles and to establish responsibility for the functions of education, research, and extension to the maximum extent possible within existing Indian institutions.

The patterns of institutional development in agricultural education and research in India are just beginning to form and to demonstrate their value. The Government of India, as well as cooperating agencies, should appreciate the scope of the institutional development that may be needed, keeping in mind that U.S. agriculture progressed through support from the strong research program and the extension activities of the USDA as well as from the 68 land-grant universities.

There are still deficiencies in the pattern in India, some to be remedied by Indian decisions with respect to assignment of responsibility for conduct and coordination of efforts in research, education, and extension; and others by action of the external participating agencies in improving the effectiveness of the cooperating personnel.

In general there has been excellent cooperation between the Indian organizations and the outside participating agencies including The Ford Foundation, The Rockefeller Foundation, AID, and the five land-grant universities.

It is not possible within the scope of this paper to review significant related activities such as the community development and other extension programs, or the "package district" program supported by The Ford Foundation, in which attention is given to applying, in combination, the multiple factors or inputs that must be utilized in advancing agricultural development. Similarly, private sector contributions are significant and growing in India, to supplement the activities of the public agencies. These related developments would well justify a separate and careful analysis as they progress and as they make the expected impact on agricultural modernization in India.

References

Bowles, Chester K. 1963. Return to India: The ambassador's view. *New York Times Magazine*, Nov. 10.

EWELL, RAYMOND. 1963. Feeding the world in the year 2000. Paper presented at symposium on "Food and Fertility" sponsored by Planned Parenthood Federation of America. World Population Emergency Campaign, Washington, D. C. Mimeographed.

HAYES, HERBERT K. 1963. *A Professor's Story of Hybrid Corn.* Burgess Publishing Co., St. Paul, Minn.

PARKER, FRANK W. 1958. Agricultural education in the Indo-American program. Paper prepared for meeting of American Association of Land-Grant Colleges and Universities, Washington, D. C. Mimeographed.

PARKS, W. ROBERT. 1963. New dimensions: How far from reality? In *The Century Ahead.* Seminar on Agricultural Administration in the U.S. Land Grant System. Colorado State University, Fort Collins, Colo.

ROSTOW, WALT W. 1963. Agriculture's role in economic development. *Foreign Agriculture,* Sept. 2.

SHAW, BYRON T. 1963. The research programs of the USDA. Statement before the U.S. House of Representatives Select Committee on Government Research, Nov. 19.

USDA. 1963. *USDA Employee News Bulletin,* Nov. 6.

AID. 1962. *A Case Study. Agricultural Universities Development in India, 1956 through 1962.* Project 386-AA-11-AE (formerly 386-11-028 and -147). U.S. Agency for International Development, Washington, D. C.

ICAR. 1955. *Report of the Joint Indo-American Team on Agricultural Research and Education.* Indian Council of Agricultural Research, New Delhi.

ICAR. 1962. *Agricultural Universities in India.* Ministry of Food and Agriculture (Indian Council of Agricultural Research), New Delhi.

Economic Growth from Traditional Agriculture

THEODORE W. SCHULTZ

Professor of Economics, The University of Chicago, Chicago, Illinois

WHATEVER THE REASON, it is much easier for a poor country to acquire a modern steel mill than a modern agriculture. When it wants a steel mill, whether for production or for prestige, it can turn to Europeans, Russians, or Americans with assurance that it will get what it wants. But to whom can a poor country turn with confidence when it wants a modern agriculture, knowing that what it gets will be successful? To the Soviet Union? Surely this would be carrying ideology too far. Of course, the place to turn is to one of the countries in which agriculture is making a large contribution to economic growth. Thus we qualify. Our product is modern agriculture and we are in the export business. But our product has not performed well abroad. What are the reasons?

Why are we, as builders of agriculture, not skilled in undertaking this task abroad? We are renowned for our land-grant agricultural colleges, experiment stations, and extension services and for the U.S. Department of Agriculture. We place a high value on the industries that supply agricultural inputs and that process and distribute farm products, on the network of communications that serves farm people, and on the abilities of farmers, although we often overlook the importance of the schooling of farm people. Yet seemingly we do not know how to institutionalize this type of public-private approach abroad.

It cannot be said that we have not been trying to help poor countries modernize their agriculture, for we have committed large sums and much talent to this task. Our government for over two decades has been engaged in technical assistance to agriculture.

185

Our leading foundations have been pioneers. Our agricultural colleges have undertaken counterpart work abroad. We are involved in country planning to achieve, among other things, increases in agricultural production. We are also involved in land reform, the establishment of rural credit institutions, community development programs, and other types of agricultural extension services, technical assistance to agriculture, university contracts, and an array of specialized training programs. But despite all these programs and this talent, the plain fact of the matter is that these approaches have so far not achieved results that come even close to expectations. There is understandably a growing doubt both among ourselves and among leaders in countries abroad whether we are efficient in these matters. What accounts for this apparent lack of success?

One difficulty in answering this question is that there are too many explanations. There are those who believe it stems out of our failure to understand the real basis of the success of U.S. agriculture. It could be that we have as yet not identified the institutional components that matter most. It could also be true that we have had wholly unwarranted expectations as to what can be accomplished in any short period of time. The way we reckon costs and returns may be inadequate and therefore the test of our efficiency may be defective. But regardless of the source of the difficulty, some programs are undoubtedly better than others. Meanwhile the present danger is that since we and the governments concerned are unable to rate these programs correctly, even the best of them may lose support or even be discontinued altogether. It is therefore imperative that we take stock. What then accounts for this lack of success?

To find an answer to this question and to indicate what needs to be done, I shall proceed as follows:

First, state the economic basis of traditional agriculture;

Second, show where private profit activities require complementary public activities;

Third, establish the reasons for the lack of success of most programs to modernize agriculture in poor countries;

Fourth, present the essential components of an efficient approach.

ECONOMIC BASIS OF TRADITIONAL AGRICULTURE

The core of my book, *Transforming Traditional Agriculture,*[1] is an analysis of the economic basis of the sources of growth from agriculture. I shall therefore only summarize the logic and the empirical results with respect to two crucial economic properties.

First, it will come as a surprise to find that farmers in poor countries are in general not inefficient in using (allocating) the agricultural factors of production that they have at their disposal. Yet the reason once understood is simple. These farmers are as a rule subject to particular economic restraints that are typical of traditional agriculture; specifically, they are subject to a set of preferences for acquiring and holding wealth, and to a state of the arts, both of which have remained virtually constant for generations. As a consequence they have long since attained a type of stationary equilibrium. Thus the popular assumption that a different (better?) allocation of the existing poor collection of agricultural factors in these communities would substantially increase agricultural production is inconsistent both with economic logic as applied to the behavior of farmers in such an equilibrium and with the available empirical evidence. Strange as it may seem, it is true that on the basis of a strict allocative test, these farmers are more efficient than farmers in most of modern agriculture, because the latter are in a state of disequilibrium, a consequence of their "too rapid progress."

Second, when it comes to investment to increase agricultural production, farmers who are bound by traditional agriculture have in general exhausted all profitable opportunities to invest in the agricultural factors at their disposal. This means that the marginal rate of return to investment in agricultural factors of the type which farmers have long been using is low, so low that there is little or no incentive to save and invest. Therefore economic growth from traditional agriculture is very expensive. It means, in practical terms, that adding a few more wells and ditches for irrigation, several more draft animals and implements, and other forms of reproducible capital of the type farmers have been using for gen-

[1] Yale University Press, New Haven, Conn., 1964.

erations will increase agricultural production very little, so little in fact that it yields an unattractive rate of return.

These two economic properties are basic in understanding the behavior of farmers in traditional agriculture. As I build on them, let me refer to the first property as *efficient allocation* and to the second as *unrewarding investment opportunities*. What they imply for economic growth from agriculture in many poor countries is both real and relevant. Programs aimed solely at improving the economic efficiency of farmers are doomed to fail. Let me repeat: paradoxical as it may seem, farmers in traditional agriculture are generally more efficient by strict economic standards than farmers in the technically advanced countries in using the particular collection of land, labor, and material reproducible capital that they each have at their disposal. Likewise, programs designed solely to induce farmers in traditional agriculture to increase their investment in precisely the same type of agricultural factors they have been using for generations will fail for lack of acceptance, simply because the pay-off is too low.

What then are the rewarding sources of economic growth from the type of agriculture under consideration? Is it more land? In old, long-settled communities with no open frontiers, additional land suitable for cultivation is hard to come by. Some, yes; for even in India it appears that a part of the recent increases in agricultural production has come from this source. But it is not likely to be nearly so important a source during the next ten years. In some parts of Latin America, notably in Brazil, new roads are opening new land for settlement. In general, however, increases in agricultural production will have to come from the vast areas of land already under cultivation, especially so in the long-settled poor countries.

Additional irrigation is on approximately the same economic footing as land. India, for example, already has three times as much land under irrigation as Japan, measured on a per capita basis. Yet India has invested large sums during recent years in still more irrigation. Had India invested enough of these sums to develop a low-cost efficient fertilizer industry, the pay-off undoubtedly would have been much higher in terms of profitable increases in agricultural production. But in Mexico, which is clearly an exception in this respect, irrigation facilities have been an important source of economic growth from agriculture. Additional draft animals, implements, and related tools and facilities of the type now being used in poor countries, as already noted, are unpromising sources of economic growth.

It will be helpful at this point to distinguish between agricultural inputs that originate within agriculture and those that are supplied from outside of agriculture. With few exceptions, all the inputs that farmers in poor countries can produce for themselves are low pay-off sources. On the other hand, virtually all agricultural inputs that hold real promise must come from outside of agriculture. This is obvious for commercial fertilizer, machinery, tractors, insecticides, and the development of genetically superior plants and animals. Though less obvious, it is also true for schooling and other means to improve the skills of farm people.

The high-pay-off sources are predominantly *improvements in the quality of agricultural inputs;* these inputs can be acquired by farmers only from nonfarm firms and from agencies engaged in agricultural research, extension work, and schooling. It is therefore necessary to develop ways and means of improving the quality not only of the material reproducible inputs, but also of human agents engaged in farming. Thus far, in our attempts to assist poor countries in modernizing their agriculture, we have been vague and uncertain with regard to these sources of economic growth, and where we have happened to concentrate on the correct objective, we have with few exceptions failed to do things in the right order and in ways that would institutionalize the process.

The people who build steel mills may have the easier task, but clearly they also have demonstrated that they have a better concept of what needs to be done than we have had for modernizing agriculture.

Where Economic Incentives Are Weak

Two factors hold the key to economic growth from farming. They are, first, improving the quality of agriculture inputs, and, second, supplying them at a price that will make it worth while for farmers to acquire them and to learn how to use them efficiently. But firms for profit unassisted by research, schooling, and extension work are too weak to turn this key. What this means is that a pure

market approach is not sufficient. Although there is a good deal of
tilting at ideological windmills in the area of economic policy, there
is fortunately little of it in the case of agricultural research, extension work, and schooling for farm children by Americans who have
had their apprenticeship in institutions that serve U.S. agriculture.
The reasons why the economic incentives of firms for profit in
the nonfarm sectors are frequently weak when it comes to supplying inputs to modernize agriculture will be presented shortly.

Before turning to them, there are two preliminary issues with
respect to economic incentives which I must consider in order to
forestall being misunderstood. By weak incentives I do not mean
that farmers in poor countries are not responsive to prices. The
doctrine that farmers in poor countries either are indifferent or
respond perversely to changes in prices, including the terms on
which credit is available, is patently false and harmful. Price policies based on it always impair the efficiency of agriculture.

Not enough attention has been given to product and factor prices
in our efforts to assist countries in modernizing their agriculture.
Where product prices are suppressed or where they thwart farmers, no program however well conceived and administered can
succeed. It should be obvious that where the price of fertilizer is
too high relative to the price of the farm product, no extension program can be devised that will induce farmers to use more fertilizer.
Farmers will not and of course should not apply additional fertilizer under these circumstances. In Japan, where farmers apply a
hundred times as much fertilizer per acre as do farmers in India,
the price of fertilizer is vastly lower in relation to the price of farm
products. It takes less than half as many pounds of wheat in Japan
to buy a pound of nitrogenous fertilizer as it does in India (see
Tables I and II). In the case of rice, the differences in prices are
even larger. Rice farmers in India pay between three and four times
as much for fertilizer as do farmers in Japan in terms of the price
that they receive for rice, while the farmers in Thailand pay more
than five times as much. Little wonder then that farmers in India [2]
and Thailand find fertilizer unprofitable.

---

[2] In India the price of sugar cane and apparently also of potatoes relative to the
price of fertilizer has been attractive to farmers, to judge from their recent production behavior.

TABLE I. Fertilizer and farm product prices:

Comparisons by commodities and countries, 1960–1961

(Source: FAO, *Production Yearbook, 1961,* Vol. 15)

Country	Price paid by farmers for fertilizer, 1960–1961 [a] (U.S. dollars per 100 kg)			Price received by farmers for products, 1960 (U.S. dollars per 100 kg)	Ratio of fertilizer price to product price		
	Nitrogenous	Phosphate	Potash		(1/4)	(2/4)	(3/4)
	(1)	(2)	(3)	(4)	(5)	(6)	(7)
			Wheat [b]				
India	37.00 [c]	26.20 [e]		6.75 [d]	5.48	3.88	
Japan	24.70	21.90	9.20	10.40	2.38	2.11	0.88
France	30.00	21.50	8.30	8.10	3.70	2.65	1.02
U.S. [e]	26.90	19.70	9.40	6.40	4.20	3.08	1.47
			Rice [f]				
India	37.00	26.20		7.80 [g]	4.74	3.36	
Japan	24.70	21.90	9.20	19.30	1.28	1.13	0.48
U.S. [e]	26.90	19.70	9.40	10.10	2.66	1.95	0.93
			Corn [h]				
India	37.00	26.20		5.30	6.98	4.94	
U.S. [e]	26.90	19.70	9.40	4.10	6.56	4.80	2.29
			Sugar cane [i]				
India	37.00	26.20		9.10	4.07	2.88	
U.S. [e]	26.90	19.70	9.40	9.50	2.83	2.07	0.99

[a] Table 174, FAO source. Prices paid by farmers for bagged fertilizer on a plant nutrient basis.

[b] Producer price, 1960. Table 126, FAO source.

[c] 1959–1960.

[d] 78.5 per cent of the wholesale price in Table 126, FAO source. For adjustment, see *Indian J. Agr. Econ., 17,* 81–84, Jan.–Mar. 1962.

[e] Average of bagged and bulk.

[f] Producer paddy price, 1960. Table 133, FAO source.

[g] 83 per cent of the wholesale price of coarse rice shown in Table 133, FAO source. See *Indian J. Agr. Econ., 17,* Table 1, p. 48, and Appendix 1, pp. 51–52, Jan.–Mar. 1962, for adjustment, based on 1957–1958, Bolpur market seasonal distribution.

[h] Producer price, 1960. Table 130, FAO source, India wholesale price adjusted to a 75 per cent basis.

[i] From Table 134 of FAO source.

There are also the probable adverse effects of Public Law 480 exports, not only upon world prices, but, more important in relation to the task at hand, upon farm product prices in some of the poor countries receiving large quantities of P.L. 480 products from the

TABLE II.　Fertilizer and rice prices in eight countries, 1960–1961

(Source: FAO, *Production Yearbook, 1961,* Vol. 15, Tables 133 and 174)

Country	Prices paid by farmers for nitrogenous fertilizer (U.S. dollars per kg)	Prices received by farmers for rice [a] (U.S. dollars per kg)	Ratio (1/2)	Index based on Japan (128 = 100)
	(1)	(2)	(3)	(4)
Japan	24.70	19.30	1.28	*100*
Italy	21.00	9.30	2.26	177
U.S.	26.90	10.10	2.66	208
Ceylon	36.80	12.10	3.04	238
India	37.00	7.80	4.74	370
Thailand	27.90	4.30	6.49	507
U.A.R.	40.30	5.20	7.75	605
Burma	28.60	3.00	9.53	745

[a] The figure for Japan includes package. The figure for Thailand is the wholesale price in Bangkok.

United States. Although the total quantity of resources available to the receiving country for economic growth is increased, the P.L. 480 imports are likely to depress particular farm product prices within the receiving country somewhat below what they otherwise would have been, and to this extent the economic incentives to farmers to increase agricultural products are impaired. We are indeed remiss if we fail to detect and help correct the underpricing of farm products and the overpricing of agricultural inputs so widespread in poor countries.

The other preliminary issue pertains to the economic incentives influencing farmers who are bound by traditional agriculture, even though there were no overt policies causing the types of underpricing and overpricing referred to above. The economic basis for the observable allocative efficiency and for the unrewarding investment opportunities has already been presented. The implication is that farmers situated in such a penny economy use the existing poor collection of agricultural resources so that every penny counts; measured in economic terms, marginal costs and returns are equated exceedingly fine. These farmers accordingly have exhausted for all practical purposes the gains to be had from economic efficiency. They also have exhausted the gains to be had from additional investment in agricultural factors of production of the type that have long been at their disposal. The state of arts available to them has been pursued to its outer limit in equating with a penny fineness marginal preferences to save and marginal rates of return to investment.

Returning now to the key issue, why is it that firms for profit unassisted by nonprofit agencies that concentrate on agricultural research, extension work, and schooling are not capable of modernizing agriculture efficiently? The answer is really quite simple. The benefits from these activities accrue in substantial part to individuals and firms other than those who produce them. This means that if firms for profit were to undertake them, they would be saddled with all the costs but they would not be able to capture all the returns. Therefore, they would enter upon agricultural research, schooling, and extension work only up to the point where that part of the marginal returns which accrued to them would cover their marginal costs. Since there are substantial additional (social) returns which firms for profit cannot capture, it is a mistake to expect such firms to pursue these activities to their social optimum. Clearly, then, the basic economic reason why firms for profit cannot attain a social optimum in this respect is simply a consequence of the fact that it is impossible for them to capture all the benefits that flow from these particular activities.

THE LACK OF SUCCESS AND THE REASONS FOR IT

I began with a judgment that as builders of agriculture we have not done well in poor countries. But have our agricultural programs abroad really been as unsuccessful as I have implied? I would be the first to concede that the available evidence is not good enough for strong inferences. Relevant data are hard to come by. It is unfortunately true that no one has had the foresight to see the experimental nature of these programs, and thus no one has kept the necessary records that would provide a basis for drawing inferences from these experiments.

But there is some evidence to back my judgment. It is implicit in the weak association between increases in agricultural production in foreign countries and what we have been doing for agriculture in those countries. With one or two exceptions, the most impressive increases in agricultural production since the war have occurred in countries where we have had no programs. Japan and Israel have been among the most successful. So have Austria and Greece in the western European complex (see Table III). The U.S. aid missions to Greece undoubtedly contributed somewhat to the recent upsurge in agriculture there. Then there is Mexico, which has been establishing a remarkable record of economic growth from agriculture; in all probability there has been a real connection between the agricultural research with which The Rockefeller Foundation has been identified and some of the Mexican increases in agricultural production. The Philippines and Taiwan are often cited as countries which have done well and where we have had a substantial hand. Total agricultural production has indeed risen more there than in most countries, but on a per capita basis it increased only 4 per cent in the Philippines, while it declined substantially in Taiwan. Turning next to India and Pakistan, where our commitments of both public and private funds and of talent have been large, the agricultural sector has had a poor record. On a per capita basis, India's agricultural production is only 5 per cent above the prewar level and that of Pakistan is down considerably.

A few years ago I and some colleagues investigated the effects of technical assistance programs under way in Latin America upon the welfare and economy of these countries.[3] You will recall that our technical assistance program began early in Latin America. From 1943 to 1955 the United States contributed $44 million to agriculture and natural resource programs in Latin America, and the annual rate of U.S. expenditures for this purpose rose to $9 million. Although the United States has continued to support such technical assistance programs since then, estimates of the amounts spent for agriculture are not at hand. The production effects of these programs during the years from 1943 to 1954 should have

[3] See *Technical Cooperation in Latin America*, National Planning Association, Washington, D. C., 1950. These studies were sponsored by the NPA. Several books were published based on these studies, and are listed in the report cited.

TABLE III.   COUNTRY AND REGIONAL INCREASES IN AGRICULTURAL
PRODUCTION, TOTAL AND PER CAPITA, 1935–1939 TO 1962

(Based on Supplements to *The World Agricultural Situation, 1963*, USDA,
1963; *Indices of Agricultural Production for the 20 Latin American
Countries*, FAS, USDA, Oct. 1959)

Country	Total		Per capita	
	1935–1939 (1952–1953 to 1954–1955 = 100)	1962	1935–1939 (Cols. (1) and (2) divided by a 1953 = 100 population index)	1962
	(1)	(2)	(3)	(4)
Japan [a]	83	159	102	146
Taiwan	89	144	144	107
Philippines	73	143	104	108
India	83	130	102	107
Pakistan	103	121	126	100
(South Asia and Far East)	88	133	110	111
Mexico	47	157 [b]	70	126 [b]
Brazil	73	150 [b]	106	116 [b]
Colombia	64	124 [b]	91	99 [b]
Chile	73	118 [b]	99	91 [b]
Peru	61	117 [b]	82	98 [b]
(Latin America)	72	129 [c]	103	101 [c]
Israel	70	212 [c]	115	155 [c]
Turkey	66	122 [c]	90	95 [c]
(West Asia)	69	129 [c]	97	101 [c]
	Prewar		Prewar	
Austria	94	137 [c]	97	135 [c]
Greece	85	135 [c]	103	125 [c]
(Western Europe)	81	121 [c]	92	113 [c]

[a] Italics indicate key countries in terms of success.
[b] 1961–1962.
[c] 1962–1963.

become evident during the period since then. Though it is true
that agricultural production in Latin America as a whole has continued to increase, the increase has been at a rate no higher than
that of population. On a per capita basis, between 1953 and 1961–
1962 nine of these countries lost ground; in two of them we had
no programs (Argentina and Uruguay), and among the other seven
were Chile, Colombia, Costa Rica, Paraguay, and Peru, in each of
which we had large agricultural technical assistance programs.
Among the eleven countries that gained somewhat on a per capita

basis, one had received no U.S. technical assistance for agriculture (Venezuela), and in two of the others agricultural production has risen very little by this measure (Haiti and Dominican Republic). This evidence, so it seems to me, suggests a weak association between our programs to modernize agriculture and the increases in agricultural production that have been realized.

Let us turn, then, to the question, Why is the record no better than this? The answer depends upon one's concept of the task. There is a profusion of concepts. Each is based on a particular view and a bit of experience; for we are above all practical, relying heavily upon pragmatic wisdom, and our wisdom is based on a wide array of experiences. But such wisdom is often swamped by extraneous considerations for lack of a general theory to guide decisions and to evaluate what we have done.

A part of the difficulty also stems from a confusion between means and end. Yet it should be obvious that the basic objective is not a set of new agricultural institutions per se; these modernizing institutions are warranted only where they become a source of economic growth from agriculture. Nor is it sufficient by this test to show that agricultural production has increased as a consequence of these institutions; it is also necessary to show that in terms of costs and returns it is a relatively cheap source of economic growth—more precisely, that it is at least no more expensive than the next best alternative source open to the country.

A theory of economic growth from agriculture, which is set forth in the preceding section, provides an analytical basis for evaluating what we have done. The important implications of this theory can be stated very simply.

First, many farmers in poor countries are under the economic restraints of traditional agriculture. Wherever agricultural extension programs have been launched, based on the assumption that these farmers are necessarily inefficient in using (allocating) the agricultural factors at their disposal, it is highly probable that the programs have not contributed and cannot contribute to economic growth.

Second, there are also agricultural extension and rural credit programs which are based on the belief that farmers in poor countries are not saving and investing enough of their income in agriculture and that they are using less than an optimum amount of credit. What has been overlooked in launching these programs is the fact that there are no rewarding investment opportunities open to farmers within the economic confines of traditional agriculture. Therefore it is not possible by means of such programs to win economic growth from this type of agriculture.

It is still all too fashionable to malign farmers in poor countries. What is often said is that they have a penchant for idleness, that they are neither industrious nor thrifty, and that they lack entrepreneurship. They are said to be deficient with respect to such essential economic virtues because of some flaws in their culture. To be sure, there are serious cultural limitations; for example, with regard to restraints upon schooling. But these limitations are seldom relevant in connection with the economic attributes mentioned above. Let us cease and desist from maligning farmers in poor countries with respect to these particular economic attributes.

Third, many of the agricultural extension programs abroad with which we are identified are attempting to induce farmers to adopt and use one or more new agricultural inputs that simply are not productive enough to make it worth while for farmers to introduce them and use them. In the case of such new agricultural inputs, including techniques and practices, farmers are not innately averse to improving their lot, but they are reacting correctly because of the small or zero or even minus rewards that can be realized from such inputs. Therefore, there can be little or no economic growth from such programs.

Fourth, in short, it is highly probable that in the vast majority of situations where farmers in poor countries are not responding to our agricultural approaches in assisting those countries, no really profitable or rewarding new agricultural inputs have been *developed* and *produced* and *supplied* to farmers cheaply enough to make it worth their while to adopt them and learn how to use them efficiently. This lack of profitable new agricultural inputs is the crux of the matter. Where such inputs have become available to farmers, for example in Mexico, farmers have responded and one observes substantial economic growth from the agricultural sector.

The lack of success under consideration is therefore probably not a consequence of the long list of conventional reasons that clutter the literature on this issue. By this I mean that it is probably not because the U.S. workers in agricultural extension abroad are inadequately trained in soils, crops, animal husbandry, and farm management. It is not because they do not stay abroad long enough, nor because their activities are badly organized and insufficiently integrated into the culture of the farm community. Although rural credit facilities may be meager, they are not necessarily a primary factor until new highly productive agricultural inputs become available; it is then that credit begins to count. Farms may be exceedingly small, but this too does not account for the lack of success. Nor is it, as some would like to believe, because farmers in these countries are prone to idleness, are not industrious and thrifty, and lack entrepreneurship. The plain fact of the matter is that these programs are unsuccessful primarily because no profitable, rewarding new agricultural inputs have been available to farmers which they could adopt and use.

An Efficient Approach

What then is the time and place for extension, research, schools, and firms for profit? Is there a natural order? In what respects are they competitive or complementary? Reflections on these issues will help us see the requirements for an efficient approach. Simply pressing for more agricultural production regardless of costs is no solution. Costs must be reckoned against returns which become streams of income. Thus, additional income is the economic aim, and the critical question is, at what price? Accordingly, the economic test is in the price of the sources of such income streams, whether from farming or from any other activity. A high price, which is characteristic of traditional agriculture, discourages investment to expand production. It follows that one of the requirements for modernizing agriculture is a supply of low-priced sources. In modern agriculture the suppliers of these sources are a mixed group consisting of firms that operate for profit and of public and private nonprofit agencies. The demanders of these sources in the first instance are farmers who are dependent upon information and learning about these sources. An efficient approach, therefore, is one that organizes (combines) these firms, farms, and agencies, functioning as suppliers and demanders of new sources of income from agriculture, so that they achieve an optimum rate of economic growth.

A concept of economic growth which underlies this analysis indicates that the programs to modernize agriculture successfully must be built on the following foundation:

First, new agricultural inputs that have a relatively high pay-off are required.

Second, a supply of these inputs must be available to farmers.

Third, as farmers accept them they must learn how to use them efficiently.

With regard to the first part of the foundation, the implication is that any program to modernize agriculture must begin with agricultural inputs (sometimes referred to loosely as practices and techniques) that are unmistakably rewarding. Such inputs consist predominantly of particular quality components which become an integral part of material inputs and of human agents. These quality components are embedded in tools, machines, chemicals, soil structures, and the genetic attributes of plants and animals. They also enter through an array of new skills acquired by farm people. That such rewarding inputs are an essential part of the foundation seems obvious. Yet there is little room for doubt that most of the lack of success of our efforts on behalf of agriculture abroad can be traced back to a failure to provide this part of the foundation.

Where are these high-pay-off inputs to be found? We have relied heavily up to now on three sources: (1) the practices of the more successful farmers in the country, (2) inputs recommended by the agricultural research establishment of the country, and (3) inputs that are profitable in U.S. agriculture. Unfortunately, they have mostly been dry wells.

Should this not have been anticipated? Yes, we should have foreseen it with respect to the first two, in view of our experiences in the United States. High-pay-off agricultural inputs with rare exceptions have not been discovered and developed by our best farmers. The early corn yield tests, based on searching for superior seed corn on Iowa farms over twelve years from 1904 to 1915 and testing these seeds on 75,000 field plots, as summarized by Martin L. Mosher,[4] tell us how slow and difficult it was to improve corn yields by this approach even with exceptionally competent and inspired workers and leadership. Corn yields in Iowa, which had averaged 32.4 bushels an acre from 1896 to 1905, averaged only 33 bushels during 1913, 1914, and 1915.

Nor has our own agricultural research establishment always provided a stream of new, high-pay-off agricultural inputs. Though it has been doing so since about the middle twenties, we have been blind to the fact that for decades before that, it produced a trickle that is hard to detect. Increases in agricultural production between 1900 and 1925 can be entirely accounted for by increases in conventional agricultural inputs. The rate of increase in agricultural output was small, about 0.9 per cent per year, while conventional agriculture inputs rose 1.0 per cent per year.[5] Thus, we might well have been on our guard and not have taken it for granted that the agricultural experiment stations in India, or in the various countries of Latin America, or elsewhere in poor countries had already discovered and developed a supply of high-pay-off agricultural inputs waiting to be adopted by farmers. Although there may be some exceptions, in general these agricultural experiment stations have not yet produced large successes; in this respect they are at a stage that is comparable to our own between 1900 and 1925.

How little or how much can be accomplished by transferring particular agricultural inputs that are highly productive and rewarding in the United States, is undoubtedly something we had to learn largely from experience. Be that as it may, the tuition has been high, but we now know that such direct transfers are not a rewarding source of agricultural inputs for poor countries.

There is, however, a fourth source, namely new agricultural research. But why should it be any more fruitful than the old agricultural research already considered? The reason is fairly obvious. There have been important recent advances in scientific knowl-

[4] Martin L. Mosher, *Early Iowa Corn Yield Tests and Related Programs,* Iowa State University Press, Ames, Iowa, 1962.

[5] Vernon W. Ruttan, "Technological change and resource utilization in American agriculture," *Proc. Indiana Acad. Sci. 1961,* 71, 353–360, 1961. Between 1925 and 1950, agricultural output rose at a rate of 1.5 per cent per year while conventional inputs rose at a rate of only 0.4 per cent per year.

edge, consisting of theories and principles that have been tested and found useful. Research based on these theories and principles is full of promise. Not that they will suffice in coping with all phases of tropical agriculture; nevertheless, they represent a major scientific asset waiting to be mobilized. But such new agricultural research has been grossly neglected in what has been done for agriculture abroad.

Although our government has been actively engaged in technical assistance in agriculture throughout Latin America for two decades, the sad truth is that not a single first-class agricultural research center has been developed as a consequence of these activities. Mexico has done well, but not because of any technical assistance from the U.S. Government. The funds and talent provided by The Rockefeller Foundation have, however, played a part in the Mexican advance. Japan has done exceedingly well on her own. But throughout South Asia, where we have both public and private commitments to assist agriculture, with few exceptions new agricultural research has been neglected. The new research to develop superior wheat, corn, and grain sorghum varieties in India and the recently established International Rice Research Institute in the Philippines are among the exceptions.

There are three unresolved issues with respect to such agricultural research centers in poor countries: (1) the number, (2) the competence of the scientific personnel, and (3) the optimum size. No doubt there are some small countries, like many of our financially poor states, that cannot afford even one first-rate center. But what about countries as vast and diverse as Brazil and India? [6] Here, again, our own experiences are most telling. It would have been absurd to opt for only one such center in the United States and to locate it outside Washington, D. C. It is fully as absurd to conceive of Pusa at New Delhi as the agricultural research center for all of India. As to the second issue, clearly there is no substitute for scientific competence. The AID-university contracts in general have not succeeded on this score. On the other hand, the International

[6] We do well to remember that we, too, were relatively poor at the time when we established the land-grant colleges. The Morrill Act came in 1862, when our real per capita gross national product was about one-seventh of what it is now; and the Hatch Act, providing federal funds for agricultural research, came in 1887, when we were at one-fourth of the present per capita GNP level.

Rice Research Institute in the Philippines is acquiring a highly competent staff, as has the agricultural research establishment in Mexico. On the matter of the optimum size of such centers, all too little is known. No one to my knowledge has examined the complementarity among scientists with a view to resolving this issue. A lone scientist is absurd; a small core may be far less than optimum. Our own experiences seem to support two inferences: first, research scientists should be an integral part of a college or university, and, second, a number of competent persons no larger than that in most of our state agricultural experiment stations is inadequate. It may well be true that by this test less than ten of the agricultural research centers in the United States are of optimum size.

Turning now to the second part of the foundation, that is, a supply of the high-pay-off agricultural inputs that farmers can acquire: Once such inputs have been discovered, developed, and tested, who will produce and supply them to farmers? The multiplication and distribution of new seeds is an example. In general this is not the kind of activity that experiment stations and extension services can carry on efficiently. Nor can a ministry of agriculture, or cooperatives that do not operate for profit, perform this task efficiently. Ways and means, therefore, must be found to transfer these activities to firms that operate for profit. Needless to say, many of the governments in poor countries either distrust such private profit-making firms, or seek to build little empires for themselves within the public domain, and they therefore prefer not to transfer these essential supply functions to firms that are subject to the discipline of the market.

The third part of the foundation consists of information for and learning by farmers. In a strict sense, it can be undertaken only after the other two parts have been built. Thus there is a kind of natural order, a basic sequence in what is done to modernize agriculture. But we have repeatedly made the mistake of undertaking this last part before the other two were in place. In Peru, for example, already by the early fifties, the fountainhead of a fine agricultural extension service had been developed, but unfortunately it ran dry because the supply of rewarding agricultural inputs was inadequate. In my judgment, this is also the situation in India. Moreover, our experiences in the United States should have taught us this lesson. Our state agricultural extension services during the early years appear to have had little worth-while information for farmers. The many efforts that we made during World War I to expand agricultural production and the lack of success of these efforts support this inference. Agricultural production in the United States during 1917–1919 came to only a scant 1 per cent more than that during 1912–1914.[7] Where the aim is economic growth from agriculture, there is no escaping the fact that unless there is a supply of rewarding inputs that farmers can acquire, an agricultural extension service is an empty institutional gesture.

But the right time for extension work is only one of the facets of information and learning which are under consideration. The costs to farmers are another facet. These costs depend among other things on the complexity of the new production process facing farmers. In considering costs, there is a basic proposition with respect to the rate at which farmers will accept a new agricultural input. It is here proposed as a hypothesis: *The rate of acceptance depends predominantly on the profitability of the new input.* Unquestionably, the greater the complexity of the new process, the larger the costs. Suppose there is a new highly profitable variety which requires only a few simple changes in traditional farm practices. In this case the costs of acquiring information and of learning by farmers are small, and it follows that an elaborate extension program would be superfluous. One observes that some new inputs are so profitable that as they become available farmers swamp the suppliers with their demands for them. Though such inputs, like striking a gushing oil well, are not frequent, there is much to be said for finding and developing precisely this class of input in launching agricultural programs abroad. Drawing on our own experience, hybrid corn was such a discovery, and, as a consequence, farmers in the heart of the corn belt where hybrid corn proved to be most rewarding adopted the hybrid seed rapidly in spite of the very low corn prices that prevailed during the early and middle thirties.

As the process of modernizing agriculture proceeds, however, farming becomes increasingly more complex. Many new inputs

[7] See Neal Potter and Francis T. Christy, Jr., *Trends in Natural Resource Commodities,* Table EO-1, p. 81, Johns Hopkins Press, Baltimore, Md., 1962.

become profitable only after a multiplicity of changes in practices which require much information and learning on the part of farmers.

Still another facet of this type of information and learning is the complementarity between the activities of firms for profit, chiefly the suppliers of new inputs, and nonmarket agencies such as the extension service and schools. This facet is often overlooked in our activities abroad, despite our success in this respect in the United States. Since I have dealt with this complementarity elsewhere, I shall not enter upon it here.[8]

There is one more facet of information and learning that I can only mention in closing, although it may well be the most important of them all. Taking the long view, it is essential to see that the acquisition of new skills by farm people is also one of the primary new profitable inputs. Though I have concentrated on new material inputs, and though they are necessary to a limited extent, the fruit from the advance in knowledge that is useful in economic endeavors is to an even larger extent dependent upon new skills. The necessity for learning the skills that are required for modernizing agriculture brings us to the issue of investing in farm people. How to do this most efficiently is a matter about which we know all too little as yet. Crash programs are warranted under some circumstances. So are demonstrations designed to instruct farmers. There is also a place for some on-the-job training. But investment in schooling is in all probability the most economical way when one takes a ten- to twenty-year view of the process. What this means is that the rate of return to the costs of schooling, especially at the primary level, is probably exceedingly high, higher than the return to the investment in any of the alternative ways of acquiring these new skills.

Anthony M. Tang's[9] recent study of inputs and the output of Japanese agriculture permits me to close with an exceedingly encouraging estimate of the rate of return to investment in agricultural research, extension, and schooling. This estimate is for the

[8] See chapters 10 and 11 of my book, *Transforming Traditional Agriculture*, already cited (footnote 1).

[9] Anthony M. Tang, "Research and education in Japanese agricultural development, 1880–1938," *Econ. Studies Quart., 13,* Table 2 and p. 97, 1963.

period from 1880 to 1938. During the first five years of this period fully 98 per cent of the total outlays for these purposes was for schooling. At the end of the period, that is, in the last five years, agricultural research and extension represented about 9 per cent of the total outlays. The social rate of return to all this schooling, research, and extension was a handsome 35 per cent per year. Where could one do better than this in achieving economic growth?

No doubt some day soon in our role as builders of agriculture we shall learn how to develop a modern agriculture in poor countries and become as successful at it as the builders of steel mills, even though ours is a much more difficult task.

Selected References

•

Index

Selected References

CHARACTERISTICS OF AGRICULTURAL SYSTEMS IN EMERGING NATIONS

AGRICULTURAL ENGINEERING BRANCH, FAO. *Rural Tanning Techniques.* Agricultural Development Paper No. 68, Food and Agriculture Organization of the United Nations, Rome, 1960.

ALBERTSEN, V. E., R. BENOIT, T. BLOM, P. G. CROFT, C. E. DOLMAN, H. DRIEUX, R. I. HOOD, M. J. J. HOUTHUIS, A. JEPSEN, H. H. JOHANSEN, M. M. KAPLAN, S. O. KOCH, G. SCACCIA SCARAFONI, G. SCHMID, F. SCHÖNBERG, and H. THORNTON. *Meat Hygiene.* Agricultural Study No. 34, Food and Agriculture Organization of the United Nations, Rome, 1957.

BENNETT, M. K. *The World's Food; A Study of the Interrelations of World Populations, National Diets and Food Potentials.* Harper and Bros., New York, 1954.

ERASMUS, CHARLES J. *Man Takes Control.* University of Minnesota Press, Minneapolis, Minn., 1961.

Food—One Tool in International Economic Development. Iowa State University Press, Ames, Iowa, 1962.

HAGEN, EVERETT E. *On the Theory of Social Change.* Dorsey Press, Homewood, Ill., 1962.

IGNATIEFF, VLADIMIR, and H. J. PAGE. *Efficient Use of Fertilizers.* Food and Agriculture Organization of the United Nations, Rome, 1958.

JOSHI, N. R., E. A. McLAUGHLIN, and RALPH W. PHILLIPS. *Types and Breeds of African Cattle.* Agricultural Study No. 37, Food and Agriculture Organization of the United Nations, Rome, 1957.

JOSHI, N. R., and RALPH W. PHILLIPS. *Zebu Cattle of India and Pakistan.* Agricultural Study No. 19, Food and Agriculture Organization of the United Nations, Rome, 1953.

KOSIKOWSKI, F. V., and G. MOCQUOT. *Advances in Cheese Technology.* Agricultural Study No. 38, Food and Agriculture Organization of the United Nations, Rome, 1958.

LONG, ERVEN J. The economic basis of land reform in underdeveloped economies. *Land Econ.,* May 1961.

LONG, ERVEN J. The family farm: Problems in foreign policy. *J. Farm Econ.,* May 1962.

MANN, I. *Meat Handling in Underdeveloped Countries: Slaughter and Preservation*. Agricultural Development Paper No. 70, Food and Agriculture Organization of the United Nations, Rome, 1960.

OGURA, TAKEKAZU. *Agricultural Development in Modern Japan*. Fuji Publishing Co., Tokyo, 1963.

PARKER, FRANK W., and W. E. HENDRIX. Foundations for agrarian development. In *Symposium on Rural Development—CENTO*, 1963.

PAWLEY, WALTER H. *Possibilities of Increasing World Food Production*. FFHC Basic Study No. 10, Food and Agriculture Organization of the United Nations, Rome, 1963.

PHILLIPS, RALPH W. (Scientific Secretary). *Summary of Proceedings on Agriculture of the United Nations Conference on the Application of Science and Technology for the Benefit of Less Developed Areas*. FAO World Food Congress Background Paper WFC/63/BP/UNCSAT, Food and Agriculture Organization of the United Nations, Rome, 1963.

PHILLIPS, RALPH W., RAY G. JOHNSON, and RAYMOND T. MOYER. *The Livestock of China*. Publication No. 2249, Far Eastern Series 9, U.S. Department of State, Washington, D. C., 1945.

RATTRAY, J. M. *Grass Cover of Africa*. Agricultural Study No. 49, Food and Agriculture Organization of the United Nations, Rome, 1960.

SEMPLE, A. T. *Improving the World's Grasslands*. Agricultural Study No. 16, Food and Agriculture Organization of the United Nations, Rome, 1951.

UNITED NATIONS. *Science and Technology for Development*. Vol. I, *World of Opportunity*. Document No. E/CONF. 39/Vol. I; Sales No. 63.I.21, United Nations, New York, 1963.

UNITED NATIONS. *Science and Technology for Development*. Vol. III, *Agriculture*. Document No. E/CONF. 39/Vol. III; Sales No. 63.I.-23, United Nations, New York, 1963.

WHYTE, R. O., T. R. G. MOIR, and J. P. COOPER. *Grasses in Agriculture*. Agricultural Study No. 42, Food and Agriculture Organization of the United Nations, Rome, 1959.

WHYTE, R. O., G. NILSSON-LEISSNER, and H. C. TRUMBLE. *Legumes in Agriculture*. Agricultural Study No. 21, Food and Agriculture Organization of the United Nations, Rome, 1953.

WORLD CONFERENCE ON ANIMAL PRODUCTION. *Efficiency of Animal Production*. Vol. 1, *Main Reports;* Vol. 2 (in two parts), *Discussant Papers*. European Association for Animal Production, Rome, 1963.

World Food Forum, Proceedings, Commemorating Centennial U.S. Department of Agriculture, 1862–1962. U.S. Department of Agriculture, Washington, D. C., 1962.

RESEARCH TO DEVISE AND ADAPT INNOVATIONS

BAVER, P. T. *Economic Analysis and Policy in Underdeveloped Countries*. Duke University Press, Durham, N. C., and Cambridge University Press, London, 1957.

Brief on Indian Agriculture. Office of Agricultural Attaché, U.S. Embassy, New Delhi, 1964.

BRODY, SAMUEL. *Bioenergetics and Growth*. Reinhold Publishing Co., New York, 1945.

FORD FOUNDATION AGRICULTURE PRODUCTION TEAM. *Report on India's Food Crisis and Steps to Meet It*. Government of India, New Delhi, 1959. (See especially pp. 140–199.)

HAMMOND, JOHN. *Progress in the Physiology of Farm Animals*. Vol. 1. Butterworth's Scientific Publications, London, 1954.

KELLOGG, CHARLES E. Interactions in agricultural development. In *Science, Technology, and Development*, United States papers prepared for the United Nations Conference on the Application of Science and Technology for the Benefit of the Less Developed Areas (Geneva, 1962). Vol. III, *Agriculture*, pp. 12–24. U.S. Government Printing Office, Washington, D. C., 1963.

ROCKEFELLER FOUNDATION. *Annual Report—Program in the Agricultural Sciences, 1962–1963*. The Rockefeller Foundation, New York, 1963.

Thai—USOM Cooperation in the Promotion of Corn Production in Thailand. U.S. Agency for International Development Mission, Bangkok, 1964.

UNESCO. *Climatology, Reviews of Research*. United Nations Educational, Scientific and Cultural Organization, Paris, 1958.

World Food Forum, Proceedings, Commemorating Centennial U.S. Department of Agriculture, 1862–1962. U.S. Department of Agriculture, Washington, D. C., 1962.

EDUCATION AND DEVELOPMENT OF HUMAN RESOURCES

A Beacon of Hope—The Exchange-of-Persons Program. U.S. Advisory Commission on International Education and Cultural Affairs, Washington, D. C., 1963.

BEALS, RALPH L., and NORMAN D. HUMPHREY. *No Frontier to Learning —The Mexican Student in the United States*. University of Minnesota Press, Minneapolis, Minn., 1957.

BRIGGS, ASA. Technology and economic development. *Sci. American, 209*, No. 3, 52–61, 1963.

CALDWELL, LYNTON K. The role of the technical expert. *The Annals, 323*, 91–99, 1959.

CEIP. *African Students in the United States—A Guide for Sponsors of Student Exchange Programs with Africa.* Committee on Educational Interchange Policy, New York, 1960.

CEIP. *Educational Exchange in the Economic Development of Nations.* Committee on Educational Interchange Policy, New York, 1961.

CEIP. *The Goals of Student Exchange—An Analysis of Goals of Programs for Foreign Students.* Committee on Educational Interchange Policy, New York, 1955.

CEIP. *Women in Educational Exchange with the Developing Countries.* CEIP Statement No. 16. Committee on Educational Interchange Policy, Institute of International Education, New York, 1963.

COELHO, GEORGE V. (editor). *Impacts of Studying Abroad. Social Issues,* 18, No. 1, 1962.

DAVIS, KINGSLEY. Population. *Sci. American,* 209, No. 3, 62–71, 1963.

DU BOIS, CORA. *Foreign Students and Higher Education in the United States.* American Council on Education, Washington, D. C., 1956.

Food for World Peace. An International Symposium in Observance of the Land Grant Centennial (1962). The Ohio State University, Columbus, Ohio, 1962.

FOX, MELVIN J. *Foreign Students in American Colleges. College Board Rev.,* No. 46, Winter 1962.

HIGBEE, HOMER D. *The Status of Foreign Student Advising in United States Universities and Colleges.* Institute of Research on Overseas Programs, Michigan State University, East Lansing, Mich., 1961.

LEWIS, A. B., S. O. BERG, and L. B. DARRAH. Postgraduate instruction for foreign students. *J. Farm Econ.,* 41, 1363–1397, Dec. 1959.

MASON, EDWARD S., The planning of development. *Sci. American,* 209, No. 3, 235–244, 1963.

MELBY, JOHN F. (editor). *The Rising Demand for International Education. The Annals,* 335, 1961.

Overseas—The Magazine of Educational Exchange, 18, Nos. 1 and 2, 1963. Institute of International Education, New York.

PANT, PITAMBER. The development of India. *Sci. American,* 209, No. 3, 189–206, 1963.

SANDERS, ERWIN T. (editor). *The Professional Education of Students from Other Lands.* Interprofessional Conference, Boston University, 1961, sponsored by the Association of Schools of Public Health and the Council on Social Work Education. Council on Social Work Education, New York, 1963.

SELLTIZ, CLAIRE, JUNE R. CHRIST, JUNE R. HAVEL, and STUART W. COOK. *Attitudes and Social Relations of Foreign Students in the United States.* University of Minnesota Press, Minneapolis, Minn., 1963.

SHANNON, LYLE W. *Underdeveloped Areas.* Harper and Bros., New York, 1957.

SHATTUCK, GERALD M. The social adjustment of Latin American graduate students at Cornell University. Unpublished master's thesis, Cornell University, 1962.

STALEY, EUGENE. *The Future of Underdeveloped Countries*. Harper and Bros., New York, 1954.

Steps Needed to Improve or Develop Programs to Meet the Needs of Foreign Scholars, Students, and Trainees. Report of International Study Group Centennial Convocation, American Association of Land-Grant Colleges and State Universities, Kansas City, Mo., 1961.

The University and World Affairs. Committee on the University and World Affairs, New York, 1960.

WARD, BARBARA. *The Rich Nations and the Poor Nations*. W. W. Norton and Co., New York, 1962.

WEIDNER, EDWARD W. *The World Role of Universities*. McGraw-Hill Book Co., New York, 1962.

ZINKIN, MAURICE. *Development for Free Asia*. Collins Clear-Type Press, London, 1956.

ESTABLISHING INDIGENOUS INSTITUTIONS TO SERVE ADVANCING AGRICULTURE

ALLEN, HERMAN R. *Open Door to Learning—The Land-Grant System Enters Its Second Century*. University of Illinois Press, Urbana, Ill., 1963.

AMERICAN SOCIETY OF AGRONOMY. *Food for Peace*. ASA Special Publication No. 1, Madison, Wis., Apr. 1963.

ASHBY, SIR ERIC. Education as investment in man. *Overseas*, 3, 8–14, Mar. 1964.

BROWN, LESTER R. *Man, Land and Food*. Foreign Agricultural Economic Report No. 11, U.S. Department of Agriculture, Economic Research Service, Washington, D. C., Nov. 1963.

The Century Ahead. Seminar on Agricultural Administration in the U.S. Land Grant System. Colorado State University, Fort Collins, Colo., June 1963.

HARRAR, J. G. *Strategy for the Conquest of Hunger*. The Rockefeller Foundation, New York, 1963.

HEADY, EARL O. *Agricultural Policy under Economic Development*. Iowa State University Press, Ames, Iowa, 1962.

KATZ, SAUL M., and FRANK McGOWAN. *A Selected List of U.S. Readings on Development*, chap. 8. Agency for International Development, Washington, D. C., 1963.

MOSHER, ARTHUR T. *Technical Cooperation in Latin American Agriculture*. University of Chicago Press, Chicago, Ill., 1957.

MOSHER, ARTHUR T. The sociologist in agricultural development. *Rural Sociol.*, Mar. 1964.

MOSEMAN, ALBERT H. Food for the future. *Proc. Society for International Development.* Washington, D. C., Mar. 1964.

Science, Technology, and Development. United States papers prepared for the United Nations Conference on the Application of Science and Technology for the Benefit of the Less Developed Areas (Geneva, 1962). Vol. III, *Agriculture.* U.S. Government Printing Office, Washington, D. C., 1963.

Technology and Economic Development. Sci. American, 209, No. 3, Sept. 1963.

WILLIAMS, ROGER J. *Nutrition in a Nutshell.* Doubleday and Co., Inc., Garden City, N. Y., 1962.

Index